D0982436

★ THE AMERICAN ADVENTURE SERIES ★

THE RUSH FOR GOLD

By FRANK LEE BEALS

EMMETT A. BETTS, Editor
Research Professor, School of Education
University of Miami
Coral Gables, Florida

Illustrations by
JACK MERRYWEATHER

HARPER & ROW, PUBLISHERS

New York Evanston London

THE AMERICAN ADVENTURE SERIES

PORTUGEE PHILLIPS AND THE FIGHTING SIOUX

FRIDAY—THE ARAPAHO INDIAN

SQUANTO AND THE PILGRIMS

PILOT JACK KNIGHT

ALEC MAJORS—TRAIL BOSS

CHIEF BLACK HAWK

GRANT MARSH—STEAMBOAT CAPTAIN

DAN MORGAN—RIFLEMAN

COWBOYS AND CATTLE TRAILS

KIT CARSON

SABRE JET ACE

BUFFALO BILL

WILD BILL HICKOK

DAVY CROCKETT

DANIEL BOONE

FUR TRAPPERS OF THE OLD WEST

★ THE RUSH FOR GOLD

JOHN PAUL JONES

Table of Contents

THE RUSH FOR GOLD *is a thrilling chapter in the history of our country. It is a story of early California, of mining camps, and of western trails. It is a story of the courage and vision of rugged, sturdy men.*

This story was written to give young Americans a better understanding of how these men helped make this great country of ours a land of opportunity.

FRANK LEE BEALS
EMMETT A. BETTS

The Call of the West

YOUNG JOHN BIDWELL reined in his horse and stood up in the stirrups of his saddle. In the distance a lone horseman was riding toward him.

"I wonder who he is," John said to himself.

As the galloping horse came nearer John knew that the rider was a stranger. The graceful manner in which the man rode held John's attention.

John was a good rider and he was used to good horses. Two years ago, when he was eight years old his father had given him a fine, young horse. Since then John had spent many happy hours racing his horse along the country roads near the Bidwell farm in Pennsylvania.

Now, watching the approaching stranger he said to himself, "He rides like an Indian. But," he added, "he can't be an Indian. There aren't any Indians around here any more."

"Hello, there," the man called. He waved a

big, broad-brimmed hat. "Hello, there!"

In reply, John waved his coonskin cap with its long, bushy tail.

As the stranger reined in his horse he said, "I'm looking for Abram Bidwell's farm. Can you tell me where it is?"

"Yes, I can. I'm his son, John. I'll take you to our farm."

"Well! Well!" the man laughed. "I thought you were Daniel Boone. I'm Indian Joe."

"Indian Joe!" exclaimed John. He stared at the buckskin-clad man. "Are you a friend of my father?"

"Yes, we were boys together," the man answered. There was a merry twinkle in his eyes. "I hate to disappoint you," he added, "but my real name is not Indian Joe. My real name is Joe Williams."

"Oh, my father has told me about you. You are a fur trapper and you live in the West."

The man nodded.

"Tell me about the West. Do you know many Indians? Have you been in any Indian fights?"

"I can answer only one question at a time," Joe Williams smiled. "Come on. We'll talk as we ride to your farm."

Touching their horses, they started down the road. John listened eagerly to the trapper's thrilling stories of the West. His eyes were wide with excitement as he took in every word of Indian fights, trapping beaver, and buffalo hunts.

"The West is a wonderful country," Joe Williams was saying. "I've seen most of it. I have Tom Fitzpatrick to thank for that. Once in an Indian fight he saved my life."

"Tom Fitzpatrick? Is he a fur trapper, too?"

"One of the best! Jim Bridger is another friend of mine. He is a trapper and Indian fighter, too. He is also an explorer. He discovered South Pass."

The puzzled look on the boy's face made the trapper explain, "That's a pass over the Rocky Mountains. Maybe you'll see the Pass some day."

"Oh, I shall. I am not going to stay here in Pennsylvania all my life. When I grow up I'm going to live in the West."

John was sorry when they reached the Bidwell

farm. The ride had been too short for the endless questions he wanted to ask about the West.

But that night John had a chance to hear more of Joe Williams' adventures. After supper the Bidwell family gathered around the big fireplace and Joe told many, many stories.

John, sitting on the floor beside the trapper's chair, looked up as his father asked, "Joe, are you going back to the West?"

"Indeed, I am," the trapper answered at once. "I wouldn't stay here for a thousand beaver skins."

"Can't we go west with him?" John asked. He jumped to his feet and stood before his father. "Oh, please, Father, let's go with him."

"We can't move again so soon, John," said Abram Bidwell. "We just left our old home in New York state. Maybe someday we'll move farther west."

"Where, Father? Where will we go?"

Abram Bidwell glanced at his wife before he answered. "I hear the land in western Ohio is fertile and—"

"Then," broke in Mrs. Bidwell, "that is most

likely where we will go." She placed the wool scarf she was knitting on the table beside her.

"Abram," she continued, "there is one thing, however, I shall insist upon. Wherever we go there must be good schools. I want John to have a good education."

"And so do I," said John's father.

Mrs. Bidwell smiled and picked up her knitting. Joe Williams started to tell another story. John stretched out on the floor again.

Joe Williams remained with the Bidwell family several weeks. When he left, John wanted to go with him.

"Wait a few years, son," Joe laughed. "But remember when you grow up I'll expect to see you in the West."

John held his boyish shoulders a little straighter. "I'll remember," he promised.

The years passed quickly and happily for the Bidwells. Many changes came into their lives. They sold their Pennsylvania farm and moved first to eastern Ohio, and then, in 1834, they moved to a farm in the western part of the state.

The trip across the state took them almost a month. There were few farmhouses along the way. The roads were not good and they traveled only about ten miles a day. Three hundred miles in a covered wagon was a long, long journey.

John helped his father on the farm. He liked to work outdoors. As long as he could remember he had loved the sight of fine crops growing in the fields. Maybe someday he would have his own farm. But always he added to himself that it would have to be in the West. Oh yes, he still dreamed of the West!

John went to the little school in the neighborhood until he was seventeen years old. Then he entered a school in eastern Ohio. He was a good student and he was eager to learn. He was popular with his fellow students and his teachers.

A year later, because of his father's sudden illness, John returned home. A friend told him that a school near by needed a principal. He added that an examination was to be given to all those applying for the job and the person who made the highest grade would be hired.

"Good!" said John. "If I can pass the examination I'll have a job near home."

"You're too young," his friend replied.

John took the examination and passed it with the highest grade. In spite of the fact that he was the youngest of those who took the examination he was elected principal of the school. He was only eighteen years old.

John was a good teacher and his pupils liked him. But he still longed to see the great western prairies. A year later, when his father was well and strong again, John decided to give up his school and go west.

He told his parents of his plans. They urged him to continue teaching. John shook his head.

"Well, then maybe you can get a farm near us," said his father.

"Farm land is too expensive here," replied John. "In the West it is cheap. In Missouri and in the Iowa Territory a settler can get a claim to a hundred sixty acres."

"But, John," protested his mother, "you'll be so far away from us!"

"Let the boy do as he thinks best," said John's father. "Maybe the West has important things in store for him."

Mrs. Bidwell looked up at her six-foot son. She studied his handsome, boyish face. His clear, blue eyes met her gaze and his quick ready smile won her, as it usually did, to his wishes. "All right, John," she said pushing a lock of his black hair from his forehead. She turned away quickly. "Your father and I shall miss you."

"And I shall miss both of you. But I must go."

"When do you plan to leave?" asked his mother.

"In a few weeks," John replied. "I'll walk to Cincinnati. It's only ninety miles from here. I can make the trip in two days. From there I'll take a boat down the Ohio River to the Mississippi River. And then I'll go up the Mississippi to St. Louis."

"Have you enough money?" his mother asked.

"I have seventy-five dollars. I can work and earn more money on the way. I'll get along all right, Mother. Do not worry about me."

When the time came for John to leave, however,

he was not happy. The Bidwell home was a sad one. While he packed his clothes, his mother prepared some food for him to take with him.

"I baked your favorite cake, John," she said, handing him the package. "And there is enough meat and corn bread for several days."

"Thank you, Mother."

John took the package and stood for a minute looking at his mother. Then he put his arms around her and kissed her. "Good-by, Mother." His voice broke as he added, "Good-by, Father."

"Good-by, son. Good luck."

"Oh, John, good luck to you always," his mother whispered.

Quickly John left the house and hurried down the road. At a bend in the road he stopped and looked back for one long, last look at his old home. It was all he could do to keep the tears from coming into his eyes. Then, he squared his shoulders and strode on.

John Bidwell was on his way—to the West.

Off to the Western Frontier

TWO DAYS later John reached Cincinnati. The little city, on the Ohio River, was an important shipbuilding and trading center. The water front was lined with steamboats, keelboats, flatboats, and many small craft. Hundreds of men hurried about, some loading and others unloading the boats.

John went at once to the river front. He boarded a steamboat, which was leaving for St. Louis, and paid his fare. While he was waiting for the trip to begin he watched other passengers and their friends come aboard.

There were businessmen from the East and wealthy southern families returning to their great plantations. A group of soldiers was in charge of an Indian chief and ten braves who were traveling to the West. John thought that the tall beaver hats and ruffled shirts of the rich men on board were not half as interesting as the beaded doeskins and feathered war bonnets of the Indians or the blue uniforms and bright swords of the soldiers.

Three buckskin-clad trappers strode on deck. They paid no attention to the admiring stares of the children. Most of the people, however, John noticed were dressed like himself in the rough homespun clothes of the frontier. And like himself, he knew they were on their way to find new homes in the West. Seeing them made John feel less lonely.

At last the boat's shrill whistle signaled that the trip was about to begin. Clouds of black smoke poured from the tall smokestacks. The call of "All ashore that's going ashore!" rang out loud and clear.

Good-bys and wishes of good luck were said. The visitors hurried ashore. The passengers crowded to the deck rails and waved to them. A flutter of waving handkerchiefs and hats answered the last farewells.

The whistle sounded another blast. The great

paddle wheel of the boat began to turn. The water foamed and splashed. Slowly the boat moved out into the middle of the river.

There was an easy air of good fellowship on the boat. In a short time John had made many friends.

"Are you going to settle out West?" a man asked.

"Yes, I am," John answered.

"Where do you plan to settle?"

"I'm not sure," John replied. "Some men on the boat tell me that the land in Platte County in western Missouri is rich and fertile."

"I wouldn't go there," spoke up an older man. "The land was recently purchased from the Indians and it hasn't been surveyed. There will be a lot of trouble with claim jumpers in Platte County until the land is surveyed."

"I'm heading for the Iowa Territory," said another man. "My brother settled there. He wrote me that I'll have no trouble getting a claim to good land in the territory."

"I'm going with you," said a man.

"Fine. Anyone else want to join me?"

Several men quickly agreed to go with him.

"What about it, John?" asked the man.

John, remembering the glowing reports of Platte County, hesitated.

"Come on, John," said the friend. "Why take a chance of losing your land to a claim jumper?"

"Well," John laughed, "I certainly don't want that to happen. All right, I'll go with you."

At the end of a week the steamboat reached St. Louis, the Gateway to the West. John said good-by to his new friends and joined the settlers headed for the Iowa Territory.

The governor was glad to see the settlers. He told them that they could select the land they wanted and that each settler would be given a claim to one hundred sixty acres of land.

He advised them to select land which was part timber and part prairie. The timberland would give them all the wood they needed to build their cabins and farm buildings and keep them supplied with firewood. The rich prairie land would grow good crops.

John selected a tract of land on the Iowa River. He started to build a log cabin.

Suddenly the people of the neighborhood became ill with fever and chills. The illness, dreaded by the pioneers, was called ague. It struck swiftly and was often fatal. The sick person shook with chills and burned with fever.

John decided to give up his claim and go on to Platte County in Missouri. He started on foot southwest across the prairies. He set his course by the sun. The trip was not easy. There were no roads or trails to follow. There were only a few farms and settlements along the way.

Days later he reached the Missouri River. He followed the river until he came to the little town of Weston in Platte County.

"Hello, John," a man called. "I knew I'd see you here someday."

John recognized the man as one of the friends he had made on the boat trip to St. Louis. "Hello," he said holding out his hand. "I'm glad to see you. Tell me, did you settle here?"

"Yes, sir," the man answered. "I have a claim

to one hundred sixty acres of fine land a few miles from Weston. But what about you, John, couldn't you get a claim in the Iowa Territory?"

"I was given some land on the Iowa River," John replied. "But when everyone in the neighborhood became ill with the ague, I decided to move on to the Platte. It was quite a walk," he laughed.

"Did you walk all the way?"

"Yes, but it wasn't such a hard trip."

The man looked John over from head to foot. He glanced at the bundle of clothes strapped on John's back. "Where is your gun?" he asked.

"I don't own a gun," John answered.

"Did you walk all the way through an almost unsettled wilderness without a gun?"

John nodded.

"Well, you certainly have plenty of courage. I wouldn't have done it."

His friend's praise embarrassed John. He quickly began to talk of other matters. "I'd like to get land near your farm," he said.

"I'd like that, too, John, but you haven't a

chance to get a claim now. No more claims will be granted until the land is surveyed this fall."

"Then I'll have to get a job. I haven't a cent."

"What can you do?"

"Well, at home I taught school."

"You have a job!" exclaimed the man. "My neighbors and I have been looking for someone to teach our children. The school is near my farm. You can live with my family."

"I don't know how to thank you."

"Just teach my children to read and write," said the man. "That will be all the thanks I'll ever want. You see, I never had a chance to go to school." He paused and looked away. "That was all right for me. But I don't want my little girl and boy to grow up as I did. I want them to have a fair chance."

"You're a fine father," said John.

"I'm no different from other parents," replied the man. "We all want our children to have the good things we didn't have. We want everything better for them."

John was soon busy teaching in his new school.

His pupils, from the first graders to the boys as tall and strong as their teacher, liked him. The weeks passed quickly and happily.

Whenever John could, he wandered about Platte County. He saw beauty in the gently rolling hills, in the great oak, hickory, walnut, and other trees, and in the black, fertile soil of the prairies. The land held a charm which he could not resist. He saw men working in their fields, and he longed for the day when he would have his own farm. There was something about growing crops, he felt, that made one strong and independent.

Late in the fall the survey was finished. The land was divided and the boundaries of each claim were fixed. Most of the settlers held their land, but some lost their claims. Several claim jumpers, men who had settled on land which already belonged to someone else, left the county.

John took up a claim to one hundred sixty acres of land near his friend's farm. He was now busier than ever, for besides teaching school he worked on his claim.

In the spring when school closed John left for

St. Louis to buy the supplies and tools he needed to work his claim. He was gone almost a month.

As soon as John returned he went straight to his land. He was whistling as he strode along. When he reached his claim he saw a man cutting down trees.

John thought the man was a neighbor who had come to help clear the land. He called, "Hello there."

"Get off my farm!" the man shouted.

John stopped dead in his tracks. "A claim jumper!" he exclaimed. Then striding on, he called, "This is my farm. I have a claim to this land."

"You aren't living on it!" the man sneered.

"I haven't built a cabin yet. I've been teaching school to earn money so I could develop my claim."

"How old are you?" the man demanded.

"I'm twenty years old," John answered.

"Are you married?"

"No."

"Your claim is no good." The man roared with laughter. "You cannot under the law hold your

claim because you are not married, you're not twenty-one, and you don't live on the land. So it's mine. It's all mine. The law is on my side. Now get off my land!"

John went to some of his friends and asked them to help him. They talked to the claim jumper, but he refused to leave the land.

"The man is right," they reported to John. "You cannot under the law hold your claim. But we can run him off and get the land back for you."

"No, we can't do that," said John quickly. "The law is on his side. There is nothing we can do about it now."

"Will you go back to your home in Ohio?"

"And admit that I can't make my own way in the West? No, of course not."

"But you have lost everything."

"Sure I have," John agreed. "I'm right back where I started—with nothing. But I'll stay here and teach school. Then in August, when I am twenty-one, I'll file a claim for another farm. Don't worry about me. I'll get along all right."

California—The Wonderland

IN THE FALL John was teaching school again. Whenever his duties permitted he worked on his friend's farm.

One day while John was in Weston he met the well-known Frenchman, Joseph Robidoux. As a young man Robidoux had been a trapper. He had traveled over the West, trapping beaver, fighting, and trading with the Indians. Now he owned a trading post in St. Joseph, a little town a few miles north of Weston, on the Missouri River.

He was a tall, thin man. His long, black hair fell to his shoulders. His keen, searching eyes reminded John of Indian Joe.

"I hear you lost your land to a claim jumper," the fur trader said to John. "Why don't you sign up to trap for me?"

"Thank you, sir," John replied. "But I came west to get land, and that's what I intend to do."

"I don't think you'll get it here. But, oh—" Robidoux held up his hand. "I'll tell you where you can get all the land you want."

"Where?"

"In California."

"But that's Mexican territory."

"Yes, California belongs to Mexico," replied the trader. "What a wonderful country!" He sighed. "There it is spring all the time, and the land is rich and fertile. And beautiful—California is the most beautiful country in the world."

"Can an American get land there?"

"Yes, indeed," answered Robidoux. "Under Mexican law you can get a grant, or claim, to good land. How much land can you get here? Usually a hundred sixty acres." He answered his own question and went on. "In California that is a cow pasture! They don't measure their land in acres. They use the old Spanish method of measuring land by the square league. The smallest grant of land is one square league, and that is almost four thousand five hundred acres."

John whistled.

The two men talked on and on. The trader's glowing report of California thrilled John. Maybe this new world, far to the west, he told himself, was the land of promise and opportunity. Maybe he should go there and begin all over.

"Are the Mexican officials friendly to settlers?" asked John.

"Yes," the trader replied. "There are quite a few settlers including some Americans out there. John Sutter, a Swiss, has one of the largest grants."

"I would like to go out there. But I haven't enough money to make the trip.

"You don't need much money," said Robidoux. "But you'll need plenty of courage."

"There is nothing to keep me here and I have friends who feel the same way," said John. "If I get them together at my schoolhouse, will you tell them about California?"

"I'd be glad to talk to them."

Two nights later, in spite of a blinding snowstorm, men and women crowded into the schoolhouse. John was standing at his desk. He called out, "Mr. Robidoux tells me that in California the only snow is on the mountain peaks."

"That's enough to make me want to go right now," a man laughed, shaking the snow off his heavy coat.

John turned to the trader. "Are you ready to tell my friends about California?"

"Yes," answered the trader, "but I don't like to make speeches. I'd rather fight a band of Indians."

"I want to know about the climate of California," said a man. "Is the climate healthful? Do they have fever and ague?"

A murmur arose among the men and women, for to the settlers the heathful climate of a new land was important. All too often they had moved into swampy regions where many had died of chills and fever.

"Well," laughed Robidoux, "they tell a story out there that only one man in all California ever had the ague. People traveled for miles just to see him shake."

The schoolhouse rang with laughter. The friendly, eager people asked question after question. Was the land fertile? Could they get land easily?

Were the Indians hostile? Were the Mexican officials and the people friendly to settlers?

"It's hard to answer so many questions," said Robidoux. "Where shall I begin?" He turned to John.

"Tell them about the land," suggested John. "That is what will interest them most."

The trader turned again to the settlers. He cleared his throat. John and the people, eager to hear every word, leaned forward in their seats.

The trader spoke slowly at first. But once he had started he had no trouble telling about California. He told of the fertile soil, the size of the land grants, and the wonderful climate.

"And the people," he went on. "They are Spanish and Mexican, you know, and there are many, many Indians, too. The Indians are not hostile like our Plains Indians. In California they do all the work for the rich Spanish and Mexicans. The Indians plant the crops, tend the gardens and orchards and herds of cattle. Can you imagine," he asked, "our Plains Indians doing that for us?"

The settlers laughed and shook their heads.

"The rich people live like kings and queens on great ranchos," Robidoux continued. "Each rancho has many herds of wild cattle and horses. Once a year the cattle are rounded up and branded. Hundreds of thousands are slaughtered. The hides are sold to the Yankee merchants whose ships bring in the fine goods bought by the rich people.

"The horses! Oh, let me tell you about one of my Spanish friends. I wouldn't be surprised if he owned more horses than you could find in Missouri. Why," the trader exclaimed, "he has more than a hundred fine riding horses! And you should see him ride. He is an excellent horseman. But then," he added, "they are all wonderful riders—even the women and little children. They ride like the wind."

Robidoux paused and looked away for a minute. His eyes had lost their keen, searching look. As he started to talk again his voice was gentle.

"The people," he said, "are the kindest, most generous people in the world. They lead a happy, carefree life and they are always visiting one another. They are charming and gracious."

The trader leaned across the desk. "If you go to California you will not be disappointed. It is a land of beauty and promise. If I were young I would go with you."

"What route should we take?" asked a man.

"I would go by the northern route so I could reach the rancho of Dr. John Marsh in California. He is an American. I don't know him, but he has been out there several years. From there I would go to John A. Sutter's rancho. I knew him years ago when we were both on the Santa Fe Trail. He is a fine, generous man. I am sure he would be glad to welcome you and help you get located."

"Come on," shouted a man. "How many want to go to California?"

"I do! I do!" the men called in answer.

"When shall we leave, John?" asked another man.

"In the spring," answered John. "We can agree upon a date and then meet for the trip."

"Why not decide right now?" asked a man.

After a long discussion, May 9 was set as the day. It was agreed that they would meet at Sapling Grove, Kansas. The men signed a pledge that they would go to California. Each family was to furnish all the supplies it needed for the trip. Then, laughing and talking about the wonders of California, the men and women went back to their cabins.

John and a friend decided to share the expenses of the trip. John bought a wagon and the food supplies. He bought a gun, an old flintlock rifle, and some ammunition. Robidoux had told him that a flintlock gun was a good kind to buy. The friend bought a fine pair of mules to pull the wagon.

The news of the proposed trip spread like wildfire. Many other families signed the pledge. A few weeks later a letter from Dr. John Marsh of California was printed in the newspapers. He praised the country even more highly than Robidoux had praised it. Now families from all over the state wanted to go to California. In a short time more than five hundred had signed the pledge.

Then in March, 1841, another letter was published in the newspapers. The letter was written by a man who had just returned from California.

He told a very different story about the country. He said that it was not a land of plenty; the officials were not friendly to settlers; and the Indians were hostile.

One by one the settlers who had signed the pledge withdrew from the party. Even the man who had promised to share the expenses of the trip with John now refused to go.

By May only one of the five hundred settlers still wanted to go to California. John Bidwell was the only man who had not broken his pledge.

John, however, was not discouraged. He heard that another party of settlers was going to California. These settlers were planning to meet at Sapling Grove, too. John decided to join them. But how could he buy a team of mules or a yoke of oxen to pull his wagon? He had spent all his money.

Then one day a young man riding a spirited, black horse came to see John.

"I'm George Henshaw of Illinois," he said. "I understand you want to go to California."

"I do," replied John.

"I want to go to California, too," said George. "I have been ill and I've heard that the climate in California is just what I need to regain my health. I understand that you are looking for someone to go with you, and that you have a wagon and food supplies for the trip, but that you have no mules or oxen to pull the wagon."

"You know a lot about me," laughed John.

"I should," replied George smiling. "Everyone I have talked to in Platte County told me about you. I came to tell you that if I can go with you I'll sell my horse and buy the animals we need."

"Do you mean it?"

"I certainly do."

John let out a war whoop and tossed his hat into the air.

"Then tomorrow we'll sell your horse," he said, "and be on our way to Sapling Grove."

First Wagon Train of Settlers

THE VERY next morning John and George sold the fine horse. They were pleased to get enough money to buy a mule for George to ride and two strong oxen to pull the wagon. In high spirits they loaded the wagon, yoked up the oxen, and were on their way. By the time they reached Sapling Grove they were good friends.

At the meeting place they met Ben Kelsey, a sun-tanned, two-fisted man, his wife Nancy, and their little daughter. John and George promptly accepted the invitation to cook supper at the Kelsey campfire.

"We'll be traveling together a long time," said Ben. "We might as well get acquainted. Say," he asked, "do you know anything about the route to California?"

"No," John answered.

"Neither do I," said George.

"Well, I guess it doesn't make any difference," said Ben. "Someone will know the way."

John and George unyoked the oxen and watered them and the mule in a stream near by. Then after hobbling the animals they joined the Kelseys.

Nancy Kelsey was not very pretty. But her smile was quick and her manner was friendly. John liked the courage in her dark eyes.

The little girl was shy at first. But within a short time she was laughing and playing. When the evening meal was over, she and her mother went to sleep in the covered wagon. The men remained seated around the campfire.

"My brother Samuel and his family should get here tomorrow," said Ben. "And my younger brother Andrew is coming, too."

"It looks as if the Kelseys are taking over California," said John with a laugh. "I wonder," he added, "how many settlers will be in our party?"

"I'm not worried about that," spoke up George, "But what will we do if no one knows the way?"

"We'll get along," replied Ben. "I'm headed for California. Nothing is going to stop me."

"Good for you!" John exclaimed. "I've been trying to tell George not to worry. I just know that somehow we'll make it."

Late the next afternoon Andrew and the Samuel Kelsey family arrived. Their wagons, drawn by oxen, were loaded with food supplies and household goods. And since all the Kelsey brothers were hunters they had many boxes of traps, guns, and plenty of ammunition.

During the next few days other settlers joined the party. No one knew the route to California. But they were all eager to get started.

John Bartleson, a big, rough-looking man, was all for leaving at once. "We're wasting time," he said. "Why don't we organize the party and get moving?"

At a meeting of the settlers, a president was elected. Bidwell was made secretary of the party.

"We also need a captain," said a man.

"I should be the captain," spoke up Bartleson.

"Just a minute," said Nick Dawson, another settler. "Let's take our time to elect a captain."

"Do you think you should be the captain of the

wagon train?" asked Bartleson in a loud voice.

"No, I don't," answered Nick. "I know nothing about traveling on the plains or the route we should take. But our captain should know these things. If he doesn't we are all headed for trouble."

The men were silent. They knew that Nick Dawson was telling the truth. None of them had had any experience in leading a wagon train.

"Well, I still think I should be captain," said Bartleson.

"Why?" asked John.

"Because I have eight men and three wagons."

"That's no reason," spoke up Ben Kelsey. "We don't need you and your men."

"We do need them," said John. "Our party is not a big one. Our best chance to avoid trouble with the Plains Indians is to travel with a strong wagon train."

The other men agreed and Bartleson was elected captain. He at once ordered that the party be ready to break camp in the morning.

That night another family and a lone rider reached camp. The rider, mounted on a fine horse, was leading two mules loaded with supplies. He hobbled the animals and joined the settlers.

"I'm Jimmy Johns," he said with a quick, pleasant smile. "I want to go to California with you."

"Do you know the route?" the men asked.

"No, I don't," answered Jimmy Johns. He glanced from man to man. "Surely one of you must know it."

"All we know is that California is somewhere to the west," said Bidwell, stepping forward.

"Well, then I do have good news!" exclaimed Jimmy Johns. "Last night I camped with a party of missionaries. They are bound for the Flathead Indian country. That is on the other side of the Rocky Mountains. Father De Smet is in charge of the missionaries. Why don't we wait and ask him to let us travel with him?"

"I'm captain of this party," said Bartleson. "My orders are that we break camp in the morning."

"But you don't know the way," protested Jimmy Johns. "If we travel with Father De Smet we will be guided by one of the best scouts in the West. Tom Fitzpatrick is his scout."

"Tom Fitzpatrick!" exclaimed the settlers.

"Yes, Tom Fitzpatrick."

The settlers decided to wait for Father De Smet. John and Bartleson were chosen to ask Father De Smet to let the settlers travel with him.

It was late the next day when the missionary party neared Sapling Grove. In the lead rode the famous buckskin-clad scout. He was followed by Father De Smet and two priests. Close behind them rode several trappers and hunters. Then came five or six light, two-wheeled carts, each drawn by two mules. The carts were packed with supplies and with gifts for the Flathead Indians.

At a signal from Fitzpatrick, the party halted and began to make camp. The orderly, military manner in which the men worked showed that they had been trained by a strict, experienced leader.

John was worried as he walked to Father De Smet's camp. Bartleson was quiet.

The minute John introduced Bartleson and himself to Father De Smet, he felt less worried. He knew the kindly, gracious Father would not refuse their request. But as he met the steady, piercing eyes of Tom Fitzpatrick, he was not so sure.

John recalled the stories Indian Joe had told him years ago about Fitzpatrick. Maybe if he told Fitzpatrick that he had been his boyhood hero it would help him now. But standing before the famous scout he knew he had to depend upon himself.

Fitzpatrick was a tall man and as brown as his buckskin clothes. His muscles were as strong as the steel traps he had set when trapping beaver with the best of the mountain men.

"I should be glad to have your party join us," Father De Smet was saying. "But my scout is the man to decide." He turned to Fitzpatrick. "Captain, what is your answer?"

"If we are to reach the Flathead country in early September," the scout replied, "then we cannot take the settlers. They cannot travel as fast as we can because they are traveling in heavy wagons. They will delay us."

"Yes, I know," said the Father. "I know."

"How large is your party?" Fitzpatrick asked, turning to John.

"Sixty-nine men, women, and children."

"That's a large enough party to travel safely."

"You don't understand, Captain," said John. "We don't know the trail."

"What!" exclaimed Fitzpatrick. "Do you mean that your party is headed for California and you don't know the trail?"

John nodded.

Fitzpatrick stared at the two men. The piercing gaze of his eyes gave way to a look of pity. He turned to Father De Smet. "We'll take them, Father. We'll take them as far as we go."

"I'm captain of our party," spoke up Bartleson. "I'll talk over my plans with you."

"There will be no need of that," replied Fitzpatrick. "You'll carry out my orders."

"But I'm the captain, and I—"

"You're traveling with me," broke in Fitzpatrick. "And as long as you're with me, I'll run the wagon train. You and every man in your outfit will carry out my orders. Do you understand?"

Bartleson hesitated. "All right," he said at last.

"When will we leave in the morning?" asked John.

"An hour after sunrise," answered Fitzpatrick.

"We'll be ready," John smiled. He held out his hand. "Thank you, Captain. Thank you."

In the morning an hour after sunrise everyone was ready. The missionary party took its place at the head of the line. One by one, the thirteen covered wagons of the settlers moved into position.

Fitzpatrick inspected each wagon and gave his orders to the drivers. Then he rode to the head of the line.

He stood up in the stirrups of his saddle. "Stretch out!" he called in a loud, clear voice.

Slowly the long line began to move.

John cracked his whip over the heads of the oxen. The animals leaned forward into their yokes.

George, riding the mule, followed beside the wagon.

"We're on our way, John," he shouted to make himself heard over the noise of the wagon train.

"Yes, sir, we're on our way," John laughed. He looked back at the wagons following in line. Then he turned and faced the western trail.

Guided by a Famous Scout

DAY AFTER DAY the wagon train rolled over the trail. Each morning shortly after sunrise the settlers were on their way. Camp was usually made an hour before sunset. The average day's trip was about twenty miles.

At first, Fitzpatrick had trouble with the settlers because of their lack of experience. One man had never driven a yoke of oxen before. They ran away and his wagon was wrecked. The whole train was delayed until it could be repaired. Another man had no supplies, not even a gun, for the long trip.

Men fell asleep on guard duty. Animals were not hobbled securely and they wandered off during the night. Precious daylight hours were wasted trying to find them.

But Fitzpatrick soon organized the wagon train. His orders were direct, and he saw to it that they were obeyed. The settlers admired him. The children in the wagon train loved him.

The settlers learned to form their wagons in a hollow square when they made camp. They watered and fed the animals and then hobbled them in the center of the square. It was like a corral. The square, Fitzpatrick explained, was also a fine protection in case of an Indian attack.

Over and over he said to them, "Always be on the alert. And another thing, remember we cannot waste any time. Keep the wagons rolling!"

On across the prairie the settlers made their way. The prairie was beautiful with its bright wild flowers and tall green grass. Antelope and elk were seen every day. Now and then a buffalo herd was sighted.

Often the Kelsey brothers, Nick Dawson, and other men went hunting. The settlers enjoyed eating the big roasts of venison and buffalo meat and other game brought in by the hunters. Then, too, it helped save their precious food supplies.

One day Nick Dawson rode out to hunt alone. The wagon train moved slowly westward.

Late in the afternoon the frantic screams of a man were heard. The settlers halted their wagons. Running toward the wagons came Nick Dawson.

"Indians! Thousands of them!" he cried.

"Where?"

"Over there," Nick gasped between deep breaths. "They surrounded me. They took my gun, most of my clothes and my mule."

"Let's get going!" a man shouted. "Come on, Dawson, get into my wagon."

Running and stumbling Nick hurried to his friend's wagon. "Come on, men!" he shouted climbing up to the high seat.

At once every man whipped his team. The mules, oxen, and horses broke into a wild, headlong flight.

Fitzpatrick, riding some distance ahead, came racing back, "Stop! Stop!" he called.

But the frightened settlers did not stop. They urged their teams to greater speed.

Fitzpatrick raced to the head of the line, and on to the bank of the river just ahead.

"Form the square!" he shouted to the first wagon. "Fall in!"

The driver obeyed. Then as wagon after wagon came rattling along, each driver pulled in to form the square.

"Unhitch your teams! Hobble them in the square!" Fitzpatrick ordered. "Women and children stay in the wagons."

The calm manner of the captain quieted the settlers. Quickly they obeyed his orders.

"Now, what's this all about?" asked Fitzpatrick.

"Dawson saw thousands of Indians while he was out hunting," answered a man.

"Where did you see the Indians?"

"Back there," Dawson pointed.

"All right, men." The captain faced the settlers. "If this is a war party we're in for it. Be ready to fire when I give the order. But no man is to fire until I give the order. Do you understand?"

The men nodded.

"Now, we'll wait and see what happens."

Over the top of a low hill raced a band of forty Indians. The chief reined in his pony. He pointed to a tree on the bank of the river. His braves, shouting and yelling, rode on to the tree. They dismounted and began to put up their tepees.

Slowly a smile stole across Fitzpatrick's face, "Dawson," he asked, "are you sure you were surrounded by thousands of Indians?"

"Yes! Yes!"

"Well, this is a war party of Cheyenne Indians. But they are not going to attack us," said Fitzpatrick. He turned to one of the old hunters in the missionary party. "Take over. I'm going to talk to those Indians."

Tucking his gun under his arm Fitzpatrick strode to the Indian camp. He made signs to the Indians and the chief came forward.

Soon they were talking and laughing. The chief handed Fitzpatrick a gun. In a short time Fitzpatrick returned. With him came an Indian brave leading Nick Dawson's mule.

"Well, Nick," Fitzpatrick said, "here is your mule and your gun."

"But they—" Nick stammered. "But they tried to kill me. They took my gun."

Fitzpatrick laughed, "The Indians say that you were so scared when you saw them you fell off your mule. They were afraid you might kill one of them. That's why they took your gun away from you."

The sudden relief of not being attacked made the men shout with laughter.

"Cheyenne Dawson!" a man called.

"Cheyenne Dawson!" the others repeated.

The women and children, hearing the men laugh, began coming out of the wagons. They joined in the laughter.

"Honestly," said Nick, "I was scared to death." He looked over at the Indian camp. He grinned and added, "I suppose from now on all I'll ever hear is Cheyenne Dawson, Cheyenne Dawson."

"That's right," the settlers laughed.

Still joking and laughing they made camp. Fitzpatrick posted extra guards. He examined the hobbles of the animals to make sure that they were securely tied.

"The Indians won't attack us," he said. "They'll be gone in the morning before we break camp. But we'll be on the alert."

He was sober as he continued. "When our two

parties separate and you go on without a guide I want you to remember this—always be on the alert. Always!"

In the morning the Indians were gone. Shortly after sunrise the wagon train was on its way. The settlers were traveling northwest toward the Platte River. The trail was not well marked, nor was it well known. But Fitzpatrick knew every mile of it. When he had been a trapper he had traveled over it many times. He had helped bring the fur packs back to St. Louis.

Traveling with a fur-pack train was very different from traveling with a party of settlers. The trappers used mules to carry their fur packs. The sure-footed animals needed hardly more than a path to follow.

The settlers, however, needed a trail over which they could drive their wagons. In 1841, there were no roads and there were no bridges crossing the many streams in the West.

Time and again the wagon train was delayed while the men worked to build a road. Sometimes rocks and stones had to be removed. At other times ditches had to be filled. Streams had to be forded.

At last the wagon train reached the Platte River. The river was wide and shallow. But it was a difficult stream to cross because of the quicksand. Fitzpatrick was too wise to let the settlers cross the Platte. He led them on up the river to the South Fork.

The Platte River was unlike any river the settlers had seen before. The country, too, was different. The endless sweep of the plains stretched on and on. Cottonwoods and willows were now almost the only trees, and they grew only along the streams. It was a strange, wild country. Thousands of buffalo roamed the valley. Indians were seen every day.

The wagon train traveled two days along the South Fork. At a place Fitzpatrick knew to be safe, he ordered the people to cross. Then heading for the North Fork of the Platte they traveled on.

Mile after mile the country became more wild. The progress was slow. It was difficult for the teams to pull the heavy wagons over the rolling sand hills. The settlers wishing to lighten the loads, walked beside the wagons. With each step they sank ankle deep into the sand.

In the distance, Courthouse Rock, a landmark known to the early trappers, towered up to the blue, cloudless sky. A few miles beyond was Chimney Rock, and some twenty odd miles farther on loomed Scott's Bluff. The bluff had been named for a young fur trapper who had died there, deserted by his friends.

Early on the afternoon of June 22, Fitzpatrick rode back to the wagon train. He waved his big, black hat to signal the train to stop.

"Anything wrong?" asked the drivers.

"No," he answered. He looked into the tired, dusty faces of the men as they crowded around him. "It's been a hard day, but we are going on until after sunset."

"But, Captain," spoke up a man, "you have always told us to make camp before sunset. Your orders have been very strict about this."

"I know," Fitzpatrick nodded. "But if we go on we'll reach Fort Laramie shortly after sunset."

"Fort Laramie!" the men exclaimed. "Let's go on!" They ran back to their wagons. The children took up the cry, "Fort Laramie." The women laughed and called to one another.

"John," said Fitzpatrick, "come and ride with me."

"I'll drive the wagon," spoke up George. "Here, take my mule," he added as he dismounted.

"Thanks, George. Thanks a lot," John grinned.

Riding side by side, John and Fitzpatrick talked and laughed. John told the famous scout that he had been his boyhood hero.

"I heard about you from Indian Joe," said John.

"Indian Joe?" questioned Fitzpatrick. "Do you mean Indian Joe Williams?"

"Yes."

"Why didn't you tell me that Indian Joe was your friend?" Fitzpatrick asked. "Say, won't he be surprised to see you? You know, he works at the fort now."

Shortly after sunset they came to the top of a low hill. Fitzpatrick reined in his horse, and John pulled his mule to a stop, too.

Below, a grassy, fertile plain lay between two rivers. On the bluff, above the rivers stood Fort Laramie. It was a solid, strong fort with high, thick walls of adobe. It was built in the shape of a square and it was about the size of a city block. Outside the fort and along the banks of the rivers hundreds of Indians were camped.

"It's beautiful!" exclaimed John.

"No one ever called the old fort beautiful before." Fitzpatrick smiled, "But I know what you mean. It's beautiful because it's the first sign of white men that we have seen in more than eight hundred miles."

"Yes, that's why."

"Take a good look, John," said Fitzpatrick. "It is the last sign of civilization that you will see until you reach California."

Westward from Fort Laramie

THE WAGON TRAIN rolled on and camp was made near the fort. After supper John and Fitzpatrick went to the fort. As the guard opened the heavy gate he called to the men in the square, "Boys, here's Tom—Tom Fitzpatrick!"

"Tom! Tom!" the men shouted as they crowded around him. John was left out of the circle of old friends. He smiled quickly as he recognized Indian Joe.

"Tom," asked a trapper, "are you going to stay here at the fort?"

"No," the scout replied. "I'm taking Father De Smet and his party of missionaries to Fort Hall. I'm also taking a—oh, by the way, Indian Joe, an old friend of yours is here with me." He motioned for John to come forward.

Indian Joe studied John for a minute. "What's your name, young fellow?" he asked.

"I'm John Bidwell. Do you remember me?"

"John Bidwell! I'm glad to see you." Indian Joe slapped John on the back. "So you finally came out West. What are you going to do out here?"

"I am headed for California with a wagon train of settlers."

"To California!" exclaimed the listening trappers. "A wagon train of settlers!"

"You'll never make it!" said Indian Joe. "No one has crossed the mountains in a wagon."

"That doesn't mean it can't be done," said a tall, keen-eyed trapper.

"John," said Indian Joe, "I want you to meet Jim Bridger. He thinks anyone can do anything. He—"

"You have it all wrong," interrupted Bridger. "I say a man of courage can do anything he really wants to do. Remember that, young fellow, and you'll get over the mountains."

"I don't see how you can tell him that, Jim," protested a trapper. "How can the settlers get their wagons over the mountains?"

"Well," spoke up Fitzpatrick, "we're crossing

the Rocky Mountains at South Pass. We won't have any trouble there."

"No, you won't have any trouble at South Pass," agreed Indian Joe. "But what about the Sierra Nevada Mountains? Why there isn't even a trail!"

For a minute John held his breath. It hadn't occurred to him that there wouldn't be some kind of trail to follow. A sudden fear gripped his heart What would the settlers do when Fitzpatrick was no longer guiding them? What would they do when they were on their own?

"Do you think we can make it?" John asked.

"No," spoke up several trappers quickly.

"I think you can, John," said Fitzpatrick.

"The trail to California is long and harder than you realize," said Jim Bridger. "But if you cross the Sierra Nevada Mountains before the winter snows block the mountain passes, you'll make it. That means you have no time to rest here at Fort Laramie. You must keep the wagons rolling."

The settlers were worried when John told the discouraging reports of the trappers. One man at once decided to remain at the fort. The rest of the settlers, however, were determined to go on.

Bartleson was full of confidence. "I'm your captain," he said. "When we leave Fitzpatrick I'll take over my duties."

Fitzpatrick, standing with John near by, shook his head. "Almost any other man in your outfit would make a better captain," he said. "You'll have trouble with him."

"I don't think we will," replied John.

"Well, maybe not. But if there is any trouble you and your friends must stick together."

Two days later the wagon train was ready. John said good-by to Indian Joe, Jim Bridger, and the other trappers at the fort.

"Good luck," Indian Joe called as John swung his wagon into line.

"Keep the wagons rolling!" came Bridger's warning.

The route along the North Platte River was rough and dusty. Clouds of dust were kicked up by the animals as they struggled forward.

For more than a hundred miles the settlers pushed on over the sandy trail. Sagebrush grew everywhere. In places it was so thick that the men had to cut a path through it.

But at last they came to the Sweetwater River and its beautiful valley. The weary settlers made camp at the base of a great rock. The rock was a landmark well known to the trappers. It was one of their favorite camp sites. Many names and even messages were carved on its granite slopes.

The rock, Fitzpatrick explained, was called Independence Rock. It had been named by a party of trappers who once had celebrated the Fourth of July within its shadows.

The settlers were forced to spend a day in camp. The wagons had to be repaired and the weary animals needed a rest.

The day was a welcome change to the children. They played games and ran about the camp yelling like Indians. The older boys carved their names on the rock while others climbed to its top.

The men and women, however, did not enjoy the delay. The ever present thought of having to cross the mountains before the snowstorms blocked the way made them anxious. The almost carefree air in which they had begun their long, westward journey was gone.

Early the following morning they were on their way. The trail led them up the Sweetwater to famous South Pass over the Rocky Mountains. The pass had been discovered almost twenty years before by Jim Bridger, and a few months later by Tom Fitzpatrick.

Fitzpatrick told the settlers that the pass would not be too difficult to cross. But they believed he was only trying to encourage them. A mountain pass they thought had to be a steep, rocky path.

When they started up South Pass they were surprised. The pass was like a long, treeless valley. The trail led them slowly, but steadily to the top. It was a long, upward climb. When they finally reached the summit they were more than seven thousand feet above sea level.

"It's like being on top of the world," John thought as he looked all around.

To the east stretched the long trail over which the settlers had come. To the west rose the snow-capped peaks of other mountains. Somewhere beyond these mountains, still farther west, lay California.

The settlers made camp on the summit of the pass. It was cold when the sun went down behind a distant mountain peak. They crowded closer around their sagebrush campfires. A soft gentle mist began to fall. Soon the rain fell in torrents. Most of the settlers ran to their wagons. Others had to sleep, shivering and wet, under the wagons.

But in the morning the sun rose bright and clear. The discomforts of the night were forgotten. While the settlers were eating breakfast of left-over biscuits and meat, Father De Smet joined them.

"My friends," he said, "some people call South Pass the 'place of parting.' That is because it is on the Great Divide, the chain of mountains which divides this continent. In many ways it is a fitting name. Even the waters in the little streams will from now on flow westward toward the Pacific."

He paused. "And here your old life ends," he continued. "The mountains will separate you from your old homes and friends. When we start down the western slope of the pass you will begin a new life. I pray for each of you that it will be a good life, worthy of your courage."

The settlers were quiet as Father De Smet walked on. Then they turned to the east and looked toward the land that had been home. They were silent for a long time.

Nancy Kelsey finally broke the silence. "I'm ready, Ben," she said. Without a backward glance, she hurried to their wagon.

Slowly the wagon train made its way down the western slope of South Pass. In order to avoid the mountains ahead Fitzpatrick rode to the southwest. Two more days of hard, steady travel brought them to the Green River. The river and its beautiful valley were well known to the trappers.

But the settlers had little time to spend in the valley. Fitzpatrick kept the wagons rolling. They headed northwest for the Bear River.

Father De Smet and his party were now on the last lap of their journey. That meant the settlers would soon be on their own. And as their wagons rattled over the rough trail they became more and more anxious.

Three men decided that the trip without Fitzpatrick as their guide would be too dangerous. They said good-by to their friends and headed back for Fort Laramie.

On August 10, the wagon train reached the great bend of the Bear River. The settlers were quiet as they made camp. This was the last night they would be with Father De Smet's party. Tomorrow night, the next night and the next, where would they be?

After supper the worried settlers remained around the campfires. Suddenly one man jumped to his feet. "I'm not going to California," he said.

"And I'm not going either," spoke up another. "Why don't we all go on to Fort Hall in the north with Father De Smet?"

"Because our trail to California leads to the south," said John quietly.

"We haven't a chance. None of us knows the way. Even Fitzpatrick doesn't know the way to California."

"We are going to California," said Bartleson. "I'm captain. From now on I give the orders."

"I'm not taking orders from you," said one man. "You know nothing about the trail. Nothing!"

"Whether I do or not, we'll get to California somehow," Bartleson replied.

John admired Bartleson's determined manner. Then Fitzpatrick's warning flashed through his mind. He remained silent as the men argued.

"If we stick together," Jimmy Johns was saying, "we'll get along all right."

"Sure," a man laughed bitterly. "We ought to get along just fine. We know so much about the trail." He paused. "Well, I'm not going to risk the lives of my wife and little children in this crazy outfit."

"I think we can make it," said Ben. He turned to his wife. "Nancy," he asked, "are you afraid to try it?"

"No," Nancy answered.

"Don't go, Nancy!" the women exclaimed.

"I am not afraid."

"But what about your baby girl?" they asked.

Nancy held the little girl more tightly in her arms. "Ben will get us through."

"Ben, you can't let Nancy take this foolish chance," said Samuel Kelsey. "Why she will be the only woman in the outfit! Come with us to Fort Hall."

"Maybe we better do it," said Ben slowly.

"No," his wife replied in a low, firm voice. "You think we can make it. I'm willing to take the chance, Ben."

"What do you say, John?" a man asked.

John rose slowly to his feet. He stood for a minute looking into the flames of the campfire. Then he squared his shoulders and turned to the silent men and women.

"I hope we shall go on together," he said. "But each man must make up his own mind. It would be wrong for me to urge anyone to remain with the wagon train. If you decide to go on to Fort Hall, all I can say is that I wish you luck. As for the rest of us—we'll go on. I don't know how we will get to California. But I know we'll get there."

"John," the gentle voice of Father De Smet brought the settlers to their feet. He walked

quickly to the campfire, his black robe rustling with each step. "You are a brave young man," he said, "but I admire you more for the fine way you understand the problems of other men."

"Thank you, Father."

Father De Smet turned to the settlers. "Those of you who wish to go to Fort Hall with me are welcome. And to those of you who go on to California, my prayers shall be for your safety. Good luck. May God be with you."

Father De Smet said good night a little later and left the group. The women and children went to their wagons. The men wrapped themselves in blankets and fell asleep near the dying campfire.

Ben Kelsey and John still remained. They were joined by Fitzpatrick.

As the scout sat down beside John he said, "Father De Smet told me that one half of the settlers are going on to Fort Hall. Is that right?"

"Yes," John nodded. "Thirty-two of us are going on to California."

"I'm sorry, boys. I wish I knew the country so that I could advise you what to do. I suggest that four of your men go on to Fort Hall with me and find out what they can about the trail. In the morning I'll tell that Captain Bartleson of yours to send them."

"Fitzpatrick," said John, "I can never tell you how grateful I am, how grateful all of us are to you. You have guided us for more than thirteen hundred miles. We have delayed your party and we have made all kinds of trouble for you."

"Don't thank me," smiled Fitzpatrick.

"But we must tell you," insisted Ben. "We never would have made it—not even this far, if it hadn't been for you."

"You could have made it without me." Fitzpatrick replied. "And that's why I feel sure you'll get to California, too." He rose to his feet and yawned. "Good night, boys," he added. Then leaning forward he said, "Don't forget, be alert and keep the wagons rolling."

No Trail To Follow

SHORTLY after sunrise both parties broke camp. The missionary party and half of the wagon train headed northward. Fitzpatrick, as usual, was in the lead. With him rode four settlers who hoped to get information at Fort Hall about the trail to California, and who would then rejoin their companions.

The remaining settlers watched until the last wagon had disappeared over a low hill. No one spoke. John watched Nancy closely, but saw no fear in her dark eyes.

"All right, men," said Bartleson at last, "let's get going."

Without a word the men obeyed. Wagons were swung into line. Slowly the little train headed southward.

The settlers traveled only about ten miles a day. They traveled slowly in order to let the men sent on to Fort Hall in the north overtake them.

One night, almost two weeks later, the four men who had gone to Fort Hall reached camp. They had obtained but little information about the trail.

"All we learned," reported the leader, "is that if we go too far south we will come to Great Salt Lake. The country around the lake is a barren wasteland."

"And if we go too far north," said another man, "we'll be in just as much trouble. Even trappers have been lost up there in the canyons."

"Fitzpatrick warned us that we must not waste any time," said the leader. "His last words to me were 'Keep the wagons rolling.'"

"I'll keep them rolling all right," spoke up Bartleson. "And those who can't keep up with my wagons will have to get along some other way."

The settlers looked at one another.

"What do you mean by that remark?" asked John.

"Just exactly what I said."

"You have horses pulling your wagons," said John. "You know as well as the rest of us that the men who have oxen can't keep up with you."

"That's true," said Cheyenne Dawson. "And remember Fitzpatrick—"

"Fitzpatrick!" shouted Bartleson. "I'm tired of listening to all this talk about him. I'm captain of this train now."

"Yes, you're our captain," agreed John, "but all of us have something to say about the outfit."

"We certainly have," said Jimmy Johns.

"I can understand why Bidwell is finding fault with my orders," said Bartleson. "He is driving oxen. But why are you complaining?" he asked. "You are riding a horse. You won't have any trouble keeping up with me."

"That's not the point," replied Jimmy Johns. "Let me tell you something, Bartleson. You were clever enough to hide your real character when we made you our captain. And you certainly minded your own business all the time we were traveling with Fitzpatrick."

"Why, you—" Bartleson doubled his hard fists.

Quickly John stepped between the two men.

"Don't you see that we won't have a chance if we start quarreling among ourselves?" he said. "Come on, men, let's forget this quarrel and think only of getting to California."

"All right." Jimmy Johns stepped back.

"We hit the trail at sunrise," snapped Bartleson. "Be ready." He motioned to his eight men and walked away. Without a word they followed him.

At sunrise the wagon train was on the trail. Westward for endless miles the plains and hills were covered with sagebrush.

Day after day the settlers struggled across the country. There was little grass along the way for the animals. Game was scarce, and they watched with grave concern the dwindling food supplies. The problem of getting enough water each day, however, was the main worry. Although they tried each night to camp along a stream, they were not always able to find one.

On the trail they kept looking for trees in the distance. Fitzpatrick had told them that when the trappers searched for water they always looked for trees. He explained that it was almost a sure sign that a stream was near by.

One day the settlers traveled until dark hoping to find a stream. But there were no trees in the distance and they were forced to make camp. They decided to get an early start in the morning.

Before dawn they were on their way. The sun came up and the settlers strained their eyes as they searched for trees. There was nothing but sagebrush around them.

The hours passed, and still there were no signs of trees anywhere. The hot blazing sun beat down upon the wagon train. But the settlers, parched with thirst, struggled on. They traveled slowly in order to spare their thirsty animals.

It was late in the afternoon when a man shouted, "Trees! At last!"

"Where?" the settlers asked.

"There, far ahead of us."

"I don't see any trees," a man said, shading his eyes from the setting sun.

"I do! I do!" others cried.

Encouraged now that they would soon have water, the settlers pushed on. They rode on for several miles but the trees were just as far away as when they had first sighted them.

Darkness fell and they had not reached the trees. But there was no thought of stopping to make camp. Water! They must get to the trees!

It was almost midnight when they reached a flat, level plain. In the bright moonlight the surface looked like white sand.

They started across the plain The wheels of the wagons sank deeper and deeper into the soft surface. They were forced to stop, for the teams could no longer pull the wagons.

The men jumped down from the high seats of their wagons. They began to shovel the loose white sand from around the wheels. The men on horseback dismounted and helped them.

John, digging in the sand around his wagon, suddenly stopped. "George!" he cried. "This isn't sand! It's salt! Taste it!"

George scooped up a handful of the white-looking sand and tasted it. "You're right. It is salt!"

"Bartleson," called John, "men, come here."

With Bartleson in the lead, the men rushed to John. "What is it?" they asked.

"I have bad news," replied John. "We're on the plain of Great Salt Lake. We're headed directly toward the lake."

"We can't be!" the men exclaimed.

"We headed west so we would miss the lake," said Bartleson.

"We evidently were too far south." John drew a deep breath. He made a sweeping motion with his right arm. "All this is salt—not sand."

"It isn't my fault," protested the captain. "I didn't know we were going to run into this. I was trying to get to those trees. I was—"

"There weren't any trees," interrupted John. "We just thought we saw them."

"We did see them! We did!"

"No, our desperate need to find water made us believe that we saw them. What we saw was a mirage. I've read that often on a desert or on the plains, due to the conditions of the air and sunlight, trees and water are reflected which are really somewhere else. I'm sorry, but we have been misled by a mirage."

The men were silent.

At last Bartleson said, "We must get out of here. We'll have to turn back to the Bear River."

"That's a waste of time," protested Ben.

"It's the only place where we know we'll find water," said John. "Come on, men."

It was almost daylight when the settlers reached Bear River. They were so near Great Salt Lake that the water in the river was almost too salty to drink. But they had no choice. They had to drink it. Although the salty water did not quench their thirst, it did save their lives.

There was grass, too, growing near the river. But the animals refused to eat it for it was covered with salt.

Exhausted, the settlers made camp. They spent the day on the river. Then the following morning they headed northward again. They traveled all day and all night trying to find water.

At last they found a trail used by antelope. It led them to good water and plenty of grass. They remained in camp nearly a week, not because they wanted to but because they had to rest their teams.

Then they pushed on once again. Each day they traveled from sunrise until darkness overtook them. They had to make up for the time they had lost.

Ahead of them a mountain range blocked their way. Fear gripped their hearts as they gazed silently up at the snow-covered peaks. Could they find a pass over which they could take their wagons? Precious days would be wasted trying to find a pass, and even then they might not find one.

They decided to abandon their wagons. The animals would have to carry the packs of supplies. That meant only the most necessary articles could be packed. Everything else had to be left behind. They made packsaddles and carefully sorted out the supplies they would take.

It was hard for Nancy Kelsey to part with her few cherished household goods. It was difficult for the men, too, as they had to leave plows, tools, and bags of seed.

In the morning the packs were strapped on the animals. Then, with most of the settlers on foot, the trip began. They had gone only a short distance when the packs started to fall off. The animals were not used to their new loads, and they became frightened. Horses bucked and reared, mules kicked, and the oxen tried to run away. The packs fell apart and the supplies were scattered everywhere.

The settlers were delayed several hours. They remade the packs and finally they were on their way again.

Day after day the settlers struggled on. And day after day the journey became more dangerous. There was no trail, no grass, no game, and often no water. One by one, the oxen were killed to feed the hungry people.

At last they reached a river and followed it to the southwest for many miles. They finally found grass along its bank for the nearly exhausted animals.

"We must have food," said Bartleson. "We'll have to kill another ox."

"Let's not kill one this morning," said John. "Maybe if we go hunting we'll find some game."

"We haven't time," said Bartleson. "We must be on our way."

One ox was butchered. Part of the meat was cooked for the noonday meal.

Cheyenne Dawson and John packed the rest of the meat to take with the party. While they were working Bartleson joined them.

"Boys," he said, "let me take the meat."

"Why?" questioned John.

"My men and I travel faster," answered Bartleson. "We can stop and make camp early tonight. We will cook the meat and have it ready when the rest of you reach camp."

"That's not a bad idea," said Cheyenne Dawson. "Well, what do you say, boys?"

"Sure, give him the meat, John," spoke up several men standing near by.

"All right, Bartleson," said John. "Don't forget to have supper ready for us tonight."

"It will be ready," promised Bartleson.

A short time later the captain and his men

mounted their horses. He motioned to them and seven of the men rode from camp.

Bartleson waited a while. Then he called in a loud voice to the settlers, "Get to California any way you can. I'm through with every one of you." He waved to his last man, "Come on."

"I'm not going with you," the man replied. "I'm sticking with the settlers."

Bartleson made no answer. He kicked the sides of his thin horse and raced from camp.

"Well, of all the dirty tricks!" Ben exclaimed.

"What will we do?" asked Cheyenne Dawson.

The settlers turned to John. "What will we do?"

"We'll go on," he answered. "We'll get to California. I promise you, we'll get there."

Stout Hearts Struggle On

JOHN'S firm courage won the confidence of the settlers. Even better he made them believe in themselves.

Traveling southwest, the settlers slowly made their way. They saw bands of Indians, but were not molested. After days of terrible hardship they came to the towering range of mountains.

Ben Kelsey and Cheyenne Dawson went ahead to see if the mountains could be climbed. The rest made camp. Some of the settlers went hunting, but found no game. Only two oxen were left. One was butchered and the meat was dried.

Kelsey and Dawson returned in the evening. They reported that the mountains could be climbed, but that it would be very difficult.

"Thanks, men," said John. He turned to the settlers. "We'll start in the morning." He forced himself to smile. "We'll make it," he added.

"There's something frightening about this mountain," spoke up a man. "It goes straight up to the sky."

"I'm not worried about this one," said Jimmy Johns. "But I certainly wish we were over the Sierra Nevada Mountains."

"So do I," said John, "and we must cross them before the winter snows begin."

Their talk was interrupted by Cheyenne Dawson who had sighted a party of horsemen nearing the camp.

"They may be Indians," he said. "Get our guns!"

"Listen to Cheyenne Dawson, the Indian fighter," the men laughed. But they did get their guns.

"They are not Indians," said John at last. "It's Bartleson and his men."

"Bartleson!" exclaimed the settlers.

"Hello," came Bartleson's voice. "Hello."

He and his men reined in their horses. "I can't tell you how glad we are to find you," he said as he dismounted.

"Why?" flashed Jimmy Johns. "So you can steal more of our meat and run away again?"

"Look at us," said Bartleson. "We have had a terrible time. We met some Indians and they gave us a lot of fish. The fish must have been poisoned or spoiled. All of us have been deathly sick."

"Don't expect any sympathy from us," said Ben.

"Help us," begged Bartleson. "We need food."

"Sit down by the campfire," said John. "We'll give all of you some food."

"They don't deserve any help from us," protested Ben.

"Maybe they don't," John replied. "But we are going to help them just the same."

When John handed Bartleson some food, the starving captain asked, "Will you let us go on with you?"

Before John could answer, the settlers shouted, "No, Bidwell is our captain now."

"We're dead men if you don't," said Bartleson.

"We'll take you," said John.

In the morning the settlers began the long, difficult mountain climb. They made their way slowly up a winding, rocky path. It led them at first through forests of pine and fir.

Passing the timber line they came to a wild, barren region. But they struggled on over the steep ledges to ever steeper, more forbidding rocks. At last they reached the summit.

Here among the towering snow-covered peaks they found a little stream. They followed it for several days down the western slope of the mountain. The stream gradually widened until it became a mountain river. The rushing water cutting deeper and deeper into the rocks had formed a canyon.

At the entrance of the canyon another stream had cut another canyon through the rocks. The settlers did not know which canyon to follow.

"We'll camp here tonight," said John. "In the morning we'll explore both canyons. Dawson, you and Ben Kelsey will explore the river canyon. Jimmy Johns and I will explore the other. If either party finds that we can get through, fire a gun to signal the rest of us to follow."

At dawn the four men left camp. John, mounted

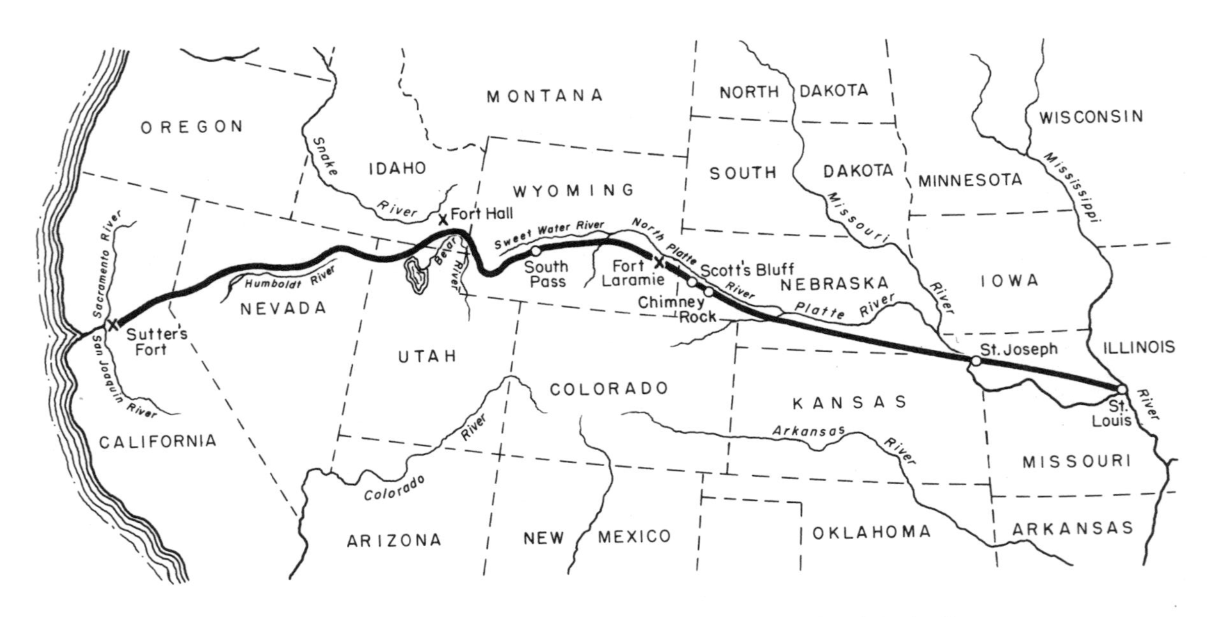

TRAIL TO CALIFORNIA

on a mule, started down into the smaller canyon. Jimmy Johns, riding his horse, followed. They reached the rocky bottom and headed up the canyon. They had gone only a mile when John said, "It is impossible to get through."

"We can make it. I know we can." Jimmy Johns insisted. "I'll give the signal." He whipped his pistol from his belt.

"No!" exclaimed John. "Don't—" The rest of his words were drowned out by the pistol shot.

"Now, we're in for it," said John. "We must stop the party from following us."

"You ride back, John. I'll go on a little farther. Maybe I can find a way through the canyon."

"All right, but return to camp before noon."

Jimmy Johns touched his horse lightly and rode on. John rode back to warn the settlers.

When John reached the entrance to the canyon he met Bartleson and his men. The settlers were just coming down the steep slopes to the bottom of the canyon.

"Stop!" John called. "There's been a mistake! We can't get through."

The settlers heeded John's warning. Bartleson, however, decided to go on—at least until his party overtook Jimmy Johns.

John rode on to the camp. In a short time Dawson and Kelsey returned. They had heard the shot and were disappointed to learn what had happened.

"We can't get through the river canyon either," said Kelsey.

"We'll wait here for Jimmy Johns and Bartleson's party," said John. "They will return by noontime. If Jimmy Johns finds a trail we'll follow him. If not, we'll go westward around the canyon. It will mean more miles of travel, but we have no choice."

At noontime the men did not return. John and a searching party went down into the canyon. They overtook Bartleson and his men, but did not find Jimmy Johns.

"He is here somewhere," said John. "We must find him."

After searching all afternoon and all the next morning they still had found no trace of Jimmy

Johns. Silently the men returned to their camp.

The waiting settlers asked no questions, for they could see the grief in the tired faces of the men. Jimmy Johns had been their friend. John gave the order to break camp and a short time later they were on their way.

They traveled as directly west as they could. Time and again, however, the rocky trail forced them to head southward. Day after day the trip became more difficult.

After they had eaten their last ox they shot crows and any small animals they could find for food. Once they were lost in a canyon. They scaled the steep slopes, but had to leave behind most of their pack animals.

Far to the west another range of mountains could be seen. The settlers thought it must be the Sierra Nevadas. Could they cross it before the winter began? How far beyond was California? Was it near or was it still hundreds of miles away?

Somehow, starving and exhausted, they struggled on down the mountains. One night, late in

October, they reached the foothills. They were strung out along the trail for several miles.

Wherever darkness overtook them they fell asleep, too tired to go any farther. But they met again in the morning and wearily pushed on toward the distant mountains.

After a long day of walking across the level plain they came to a valley. It was a beautiful, fertile valley with green grass and trees. But best of all there was plenty of food for the starving settlers. There were hundreds of fat antelope and elk and countless flocks of wild game birds.

"It's a mirage," they said. "It can't be real."

But it was real and for the first time in weeks they laughed as they made camp. Men went out to hunt and returned with all the meat the hungry settlers could eat.

They remained in camp all the next day. Some of the men went hunting again. Others helped Nancy Kelsey dry the meat.

In the morning at sunrise, John sent two men on ahead to explore the country. Then he and the settlers started for the distant mountains.

Late in the afternoon they made camp. While they were cooking supper, one of the men, who had gone on to explore the country, returned.

The man rode into camp, shouting and laughing. He reined in his poor, thin horse and swung from the saddle.

"We made it!" he shouted. "We made it!"

The settlers looked at one another and shook their heads. Finally one asked, "What do you mean?"

"We're in California!"

"California!"

"Yes! Yes!" the man shouted. "We're here!"

"How do you know?"

"We met an Indian. We told him that we were Americans. He spoke very brokenly but he said, 'You American. Dr. Marsh, American. He live near. I take you.' I tell you, we are in California."

"But the mountains in the distance," said John. "Aren't they the Sierra Nevadas? Don't we have to cross them?"

"No, we crossed the Sierra Nevadas and we didn't know it. I tell you, we're in California."

The settlers could not believe the good news. They stared at one another. Then slowly they began to realize that the terrible, terrible trip was over. They laughed and cried and shouted with joy. They ran around, they jumped and danced and slapped one another on the back. Even Bartleson and his men were included in the noisy celebration.

Only Mrs. Kelsey remained perfectly still by the campfire. As her husband joined her she said quietly, "We made it, Ben."

Then for the first time during all the hard, terrible trip, Nancy Kelsey bowed her head. Tears streamed down her thin cheeks and fell on the golden curls of the little girl in her arms.

Later, after the wild excitement had died away, the settlers gathered around the campfire. They were in high, good spirits.

"John," said Cheyenne Dawson, "if it hadn't been for you we never would have made it."

"That's true," agreed Ben Kelsey.

"No," John replied. "No one man deserves the credit. We made it because we stuck together."

Captain John A. Sutter

TWO DAYS later, November 4, 1841, the settlers arrived at Dr. Marsh's rancho. They were warmly welcomed by the doctor. He gave them food and told them they could stay at his rancho as long as they wished.

"Dr. Marsh," said John, "is a fine, generous man. No wonder Robidoux praised the people of California so highly."

"Yes," agreed Ben Kelsey. "We must give him something to show how much we appreciate his kindness."

"I haven't any money—not a cent," spoke up Dawson. "But I'll gladly give him some gunpowder."

"And I'll give him some lead," said another man.

"I'm not going to give him anything," said John Bartleson.

"Well," snapped Ben, "we hardly expected you

to do the decent thing. Here, John," he added, "take this hunting knife. It's a good, strong one."

The settlers took up a collection of knives, lead for bullets, gunpowder, and other articles. They took the gifts to Dr. Marsh.

"Thank you, men," smiled the doctor.

"We are grateful to you," said John. "After a few days' rest we plan to go on to Sutter's Fort. How do we get to the fort?"

"Go north until you reach the Sacramento River. Follow it until you come to the American River, and there you will find the fort. It's about a hundred miles from my rancho. But before you go to Sutter's you will all have to get passports. Since you are Americans you will need these papers in order to stay in this country, which is Mexican territory."

"Where will we get them?"

"From the Mexican officials at San Jose, a little town about forty miles south of my rancho."

A short time later the men returned to their camp under the spreading oak trees. Tired, but happy, the settlers were soon asleep.

In the morning John was up early. He saw Dr. Marsh standing near the house and hurried to him.

"Good morning, Doctor," he called.

There was no answer.

"Good morning," John repeated. "I can't tell you—" He stopped as he looked into the cold, unfriendly eyes of the doctor.

"What's good about it?" Marsh demanded.

"Why, Doctor, what is the matter?"

"Matter! How would you like to have thirty-two hungry people camping on your rancho and eating your food? How long are you going to stay?"

John was too surprised to answer.

"Well, how long are you going to stay?"

"I don't understand. Last night you said we were welcome to stay as long as we wished."

"That was last night," snapped the doctor. He turned and strode into the house.

Slowly John walked back to camp. He told the settlers what had happened.

"What shall we do?" asked a man.

"We'll get our passports," answered John, "and then head north for Sutter's Fort."

"I'm not going," said Ben Kelsey.

"Why not?"

"After the way Dr. Marsh has treated us, I'm sure that Sutter will be just as mean. I'm going back to the valley where we saw all the antelope and elk. I'll spend the winter there trapping and hunting. At least I know I can make a living for my family that way."

"My men and I are going with you," said Bartleson. "And in the spring we are going back to Missouri."

Almost half of the settlers decided to return to the fertile valley. They packed, said good-by to their friends, and left.

The rest of the settlers started for San Jose. On the way they were arrested and thrown into jail. But they were finally released and given their passports.

Some of the men, including George Henshaw and Cheyenne Dawson, decided to join their friends in the valley. Others decided to remain in San Jose, hoping to find work or better yet, to get land. John and three companions headed northward for Sutter's Fort.

John, riding a thin, weary horse given him by Dawson, was in the lead. The little party traveled slowly for there were no roads to follow. They rode over narrow Indian trails or along paths worn smooth by wild animals. The winter rains had begun and it rained steadily.

At last they came to the Sacramento River and followed it upstream. After a hard day's ride they came to the point where the American River flowed into it. On the south bank of the American River stood Fort Sutter.

Dog-tired, wet and cold as the men were, they broke into cheers. They urged their horses to greater speed and raced across the plain to the fort.

John was thrilled not only because he had at last reached his goal, but the very sight of the fort stirred him. Fine and strong as he had thought Fort Laramie to be, it was small compared with this great fort.

The fort was built in the shape of a rectangle, one hundred fifty feet wide by five hundred feet long. High, thick adobe walls surrounded the buildings. Loop-holed watchtowers and great wooden gates gave it an air of boldness and stubborn strength.

An Indian guard, proud of his new uniform and long rifle, stopped them at the gate. They showed him their passports and at once he opened the gate. Silently they rode into the fort.

In the square a hundred or more Indians and a few white men were at work. Some were building shops, storehouses, and living quarters. Others were making adobe bricks or sawing lumber.

John and his companions reined in their horses and dismounted.

"Hello," a short, stocky man called. He strode toward them smiling. "What can I do for you? I'm Captain John Sutter."

"I'm John Bidwell and these are—"

"John Bidwell!" exclaimed Sutter. "Did my men find you?"

"Your men?"

"Yes, I sent some men out to find you and your party of settlers."

"But, Captain, I don't understand. How did you know about us?"

"Jimmy Johns told me. He—"

"Jimmy Johns!" the men exclaimed.

"Is he here at the fort?" John asked.

"Yes," Sutter nodded. "Several weeks ago Jimmy Johns reached here, half-starved and exhausted. He told me that his friends were having trouble crossing the mountains. I sent out two parties of men, with pack trains of food and supplies, to find you. I sent one of the parties down to the Marsh rancho because Jimmy Johns told me that you were trying to get there."

"We were there awhile. Dr. Marsh was—"

"Dr. Marsh!" Sutter threw back his head and laughed. "He's no more a doctor than I am. By the way, how did he treat you?"

John hesitated.

"I know. He's an old miser."

"Captain Sutter," spoke up one of John's companions, "we hope we can stay here—at least for a while. When we are stronger we can work and pay you back for our food and lodging."

"If we can stay we'll give you anything we have," said John. He held out his gun. "It's all I have, but it's yours, Captain."

Sutter stepped back quickly. "I have traveled across the plains and mountains myself so I know the hardships you have suffered. You couldn't give me anything — ever. I want to help you. When you are rested I'll be glad to hire you to work here at my fort, if you want to stay."

Sutter called to an Indian. "Take care of these horses," he ordered. He turned again to the men. "Now come," he added. "Let's find Jimmy Johns. He'll be glad to see you."

Jimmy Johns was indeed glad to see his old friends. They shouted and laughed and asked one another endless questions. They did not notice when Sutter, smiling to himself, left them.

"How did you ever get out of that canyon?" John asked.

"I was lucky, that's all," Jimmy Johns replied. "I finally found a place where my horse was able to climb to the top. But you were right, John, the rest of the party could not have made it." He shook his head. "Then I headed north and after days of travel I reached the fort."

"Is Captain Sutter as kind as he seems to be?" asked one of the men.

Jimmy Johns' answer was prompt. "Captain Sutter is the finest, the kindest, and the most generous man I have ever known. There isn't a man working for him, Indian or white, who won't tell you the same thing."

"Does he have enough work here to hire all of us?"

"Enough!" Jimmy threw up his hands. "Man alive, it will take several years to complete the plans he has for the fort. And all the land for miles around belongs to him."

John lifted his gaze over the walls of the fort. He looked out across the fertile valley of the tree-lined Sacramento River. Cattle, knee-deep in tall grass, roamed in herds over the plain. Great fields where wheat had tossed in the summer breeze were now grown over with bright autumn flowers. Smoke from the campfires of several little Indian villages rose slowly to the sky.

"And all this belongs to Sutter," he said to himself. "It's an empire in the heart of a wilderness."

Later that night John said to Sutter, "I am greatly impressed with this fertile valley."

"Thank you," the captain replied. "There is nothing like working on your own land."

"That is why I came to California," John smiled. "I, too, want land of my own. But right now I need a job."

"I've already told you that when you're ready to go to work I have a job for you. I meant that, Bidwell. You and I are going to be friends—good friends."

Early Days in California

CALIFORNIA was ever a land of sunshine and beauty. It was also a neglected country. Although claimed by Spain in the early 1500's no attempts were made to settle the land until 1769.

The first settlements were sun-dried adobe brick missions. They were built by the kindly priests of the Catholic Church. The lonely missions stretched along the Pacific Coast from San Diego northward to Sonoma. The missions were founded to make Christians of the Indians and to hold the land for Spain. Soldiers were sent to protect the missions from Indian attacks.

The missions, twenty-one in all, were a day's journey apart. Each mission was like a little village with its life centered around the church. The priests taught the Indians to grow crops, tend the herds of cattle and sheep, and do many other useful tasks. The Indians, as a rule, were happy and peaceful under the guidance of the priests.

After a time most of the soldiers were stationed in four main presidios, or forts, on the coast. The forts were built to guard the fine natural harbors. The soldiers would still be called upon to put down any Indian trouble. Their more important duty, however, was to prevent foreign countries from trying to invade California.

As the years passed a few Mexican settlers arrived. Slowly little towns grew up around the missions and forts. Spain, wishing to strengthen its hold on the distant colony, offered huge tracts of land to those who would settle in California. A number of fine wealthy Spanish and Mexican families accepted the generous grants of land. And the gay and colorful days of the great cattle ranchos began.

Like kings and queens the wealthy owners ruled over their vast estates. Tens of thousands of wild horses and cattle roamed the great valleys. Hundreds of Indians worked in the fields.

Although the heavy labor was done by the Indians, the owners were also busy. The men rode out to inspect the fields and the herds of cattle. Often at dawn they raced over the rolling hills.

What riders they were! And why not, for didn't they boast that they were born in the saddle? There wasn't a man among them that wasn't an expert horseman.

It was a poor rider indeed who couldn't at full gallop pick up a leaf or flower off the ground. It took only a fair rider to keep his foot on a silver coin in his stirrup and not lose the coin while mounted on a bucking, rearing horse. A good rider, they admitted, was the man who could balance a tray of glasses filled with water and race across the plain without spilling a drop!

The women were busy, too. They had many servants to be sure, but there were many guests and unexpected visitors to welcome and entertain.

Often a guest would stop in to visit the family for a few days and then remain a year or two. It didn't matter for there was always plenty of food, plenty of room, and plenty of laughter and happiness to share with all—friends and strangers.

The people led a carefree life and they loved to

sing and dance. Their ranchos were far apart, but no one missed a neighbor's dance. Off they went, riding their fine horses or traveling in their clumsy ox-drawn carts, laughing and singing all the way.

Then in 1821, a change came into their lives. Mexico won its independence from Spain. California declared its independence, too, and later became a territory of the new Republic of Mexico.

For the first time the Californios, as the proud, wealthy landowners called themselves, were conscious of their rights as citizens. They took away the power of the missions and freed the Indians. They opened their ports to trade with other countries, something which Spain had never done. They raised taxes and trained a small army of their own soldiers.

The arrival of a Mexican governor ended the brief period of political freedom. There was, however, little complaint while he was in power, because he was a just man.

But the next governor was a dictator. He took away all the power of the people. He ordered the death penalty for breaking any law, even for a minor offense.

The proud Californios had not forgotten their first taste of political freedom. They rebelled and the governor was forced to return to Mexico.

Then followed the rule of other governors. Some were just and some were dictators. For years the quarrels and bloodless revolts of the Californios kept them in trouble with Mexico.

In some ways the quarrels and revolts helped the Californios. While they were fighting for their rights they were united. But the minute a dispute was settled they became jealous and suspicious of one another.

Two important leaders were young, quick-tempered Juan Alvarado and his uncle, the equally hot-headed, but more cautious and capable General Mariano Vallejo. Under their united efforts the Californios threw out a dictator governor.

Mexico, tired of the constant quarrels, sought to quiet the rebellious Californios. In 1839, Alvarado was appointed civil governor and Vallejo became the military commander.

Vallejo made his headquarters in Sonoma where he and his family owned vast ranchos in the fertile northern valley. Alvarado took up his duties in the sleepy little capital of Monterey.

As governor, Alvarado handled all the land grants. It was an important duty because each year more settlers were coming to California.

One of the first men to ask the newly appointed governor for a land grant was the Swiss John A. Sutter. He was given permission to choose the land he wanted. Sutter promised, as did all foreign settlers, to become a Mexican citizen when the land grant was given to him.

Sutter knew exactly what he wanted and he found it. The Sacramento River Valley suited him perfectly. The land was fertile. Boats could go up and down the Sacramento River. That was important because he would need to bring in supplies and to ship out the products of his rancho.

The valley was far from Mexican authority and that was what he wanted most of all. Here in the wilderness he would be alone. He would not have to depend upon uncertain powers of ever-changing governors and military leaders. Here in the wilderness he could build his own colony—his empire.

In the beginning the odds were against him. Most of the workmen deserted. He was surrounded by hostile Indians. One swift night attack all but wiped out his little camp.

Sutter, however, was not discouraged. He went right ahead with his plans for the future. Peace was made with the Indians. Work was started on a strong adobe fort.

In the spring Sutter was given a grant of eleven square leagues of land, almost fifty thousand acres, by Governor Alvarado. As Sutter promised, he became a Mexican citizen and was made a captain in the army.

Now work on the fort began in earnest. A few Indians who had lived near the missions came to the fort and asked for work. Sutter was glad to hire them because the mission Indians were skilled in making adobe bricks. He treated them kindly and even protected them from their enemies.

Word of Captain Sutter's kindness spread through the valley. The Indians learned that

Sutter was like the kindly Fathers of the old missions. He was a trusted friend, to be feared only if they attacked him. Soon he had several hundred Indians working for him.

Trees were cut down and wells were dug. Fields, gardens, and orchards were planted. Beyond the fields of grain stretched the endless miles of grazing lands. Herds of cattle, sheep, and wild horses roamed the pastures, growing fat on the rich clover and tall green grass.

Sutter's dreams were working out as he had carefully planned. He was the power and the law of the Sacramento Valley. He was one of the most important men in all California.

No wonder settlers from the United States and other countries made their way to his fort. He helped them all—rich and poor alike.

John Bidwell was no exception. But it was no small honor for the penniless, young settler to become the right-hand man of wealthy, powerful Captain John A. Sutter.

John had been at the fort only a few days when Sutter said to him, "I know you are anxious to obtain a land grant. Why don't you settle here in the Sacramento Valley? I'd like to have you for a neighbor."

"Thank you, Captain."

"Now, of course, the land grant will cost nothing. But you will have to buy herds of cattle and sheep to stock your land."

"I have no money," said John.

Sutter stroked his blond moustache in silence. "You could get a small grant," he said at last. "I will sell you the cattle you need. You can pay me later."

"I couldn't do that, sir. I don't want to be in debt to any man. I'll make my own way out here in the West."

"Then how would you like to manage the affairs of New Helvetia?"

"New Helvetia?" questioned John.

"Yes," Sutter nodded. "You Americans call my fort Fort Sutter. I like to call it New Helvetia. It means New Switzerland. I am a Swiss, you know. Sometimes I am lonely for my old home and friends." He sighed. Then he smiled and asked, "Will you work for me, Bidwell?"

"Yes, I will," John answered at once.

"Good! Now, let me tell you about my plans. First of all the fort must be finished as quickly as possible. Only then will I be strong enough to hold my land."

"Do you expect trouble from the Indians?"

"No, the Indians in the valley are my friends. I am worried about the people of California. They are restless under the rule of Mexico."

He shook his head. "I can't understand the people. They are kind and generous to a fault. But they quarrel among themselves all the time.

"Take young Governor Alvarado and the military commander, General Vallejo, for instance. Both are sincere patriots and yet each is always at the other's throat. Their quarrels will lead to another Mexican governor being sent to Monterey. I tell you, Bidwell, there is trouble in the air. But I think it will be safe here in the valley."

Just as Sutter expected, another bitter quarrel soon broke out between Alvarado and Vallejo. Mexico was disgusted with the two men and promptly removed them from power. A Mexican governor was sent to rule California. And this time the governor brought with him three hundred rough, tough convict soldiers to enforce his orders.

Although the people liked the governor they hated the Mexican soldiers. The people held secret meetings to plan a revolt. But they could not agree on anything. As in the old days they spent all their time quarreling with one another.

At New Helvetia, however, work went on as usual. John, in charge of a party of Indians, had gone to another fort which Sutter had recently purchased. They were busy tearing down the fort and bringing all the lumber, the food supplies, the guns, cannon, and ammunition, and the herds of cattle and sheep back to New Helvetia.

Sutter thought that the job would take at least two years of hard work. John completed the task in a little more than a year.

So well had John carried out his orders that he was put in charge of Sutter's cattle rancho. The great rancho, on the Feather River, was a few miles north of the fort. It was called Hock Farm after the large Hock Indian village on the rancho.

Hundreds of Indians worked in the fields of wheat and in the orchards and gardens. Scores of Indian vaqueros, or cowboys, tended the herds of wild cattle.

The cattle industry was almost the only business in California. Each year tens of thousands of cattle were killed for their hides and tallow.

Most of the tallow was shipped to South America to be made into candles and soap. The hides were traded for the fine, expensive silks, satins, and velvets, rare perfumes, jewelry, china, and other luxuries the wealthy people loved.

The goods were brought in on the boats of English, French, and American merchants. The shrewd Yankee merchants, however, did the greatest share of the business.

For John these were exciting, busy years. Since he was Sutter's right-hand man and personal friend, he knew all the prominent men in California. He met Lieutenant John C. Frémont of the United States Army and his party at Sutter's Fort.

Frémont claimed to be on an exploring trip. There were rumors, however, that he was trying to find out the strength and weakness of the Mexican government in California. He remained only a short time and then returned East. But his visit continued to disturb the Mexican officials.

Other rumors disturbed the settlers. It was said that their land grants were to be taken from them and that they would be told to leave California. There was much talk against the Americans who each year were coming in greater numbers. There was even some talk that Sutter was too powerful and that he would have to be watched.

Sutter was not a man to remain quiet when action was needed. He went to the governor and bluntly demanded the truth. The governor was friendly and told him that the rumors were false. The governor gave him permission to ask for another land grant of eleven square leagues. Sutter was also given the right to issue grants to worthy settlers who wanted land in his valley.

Sutter pledged his loyalty to the governor and returned to his fort. The people, trusting the promise of the governor, were quieted and they, too, pledged their loyalty to him.

A few months later, in the fall of 1844, the long-expected revolt took place. The governor and his hated soldiers were defeated and shipped back to Mexico.

Sutter, Bidwell, and almost two hundred men living in the Sacramento Valley had fought with the governor.

Sutter was arrested by the victorious Californios. He proved that he was obeying the orders of the Mexican governor. He was freed when he promised to be loyal to the new governor already elected by the patriots.

Sutter and his men started back to the Sacramento Valley. On the way Sutter said, "Bidwell, Mexico has lost this country. Some day California will belong to the United States."

"I hope you're right," John replied looking out across the country. "This is a beautiful, fertile land. It is a land of great promise."

A Bear Stands and Fights

THE SUMMER days of 1845 passed quickly at Fort Sutter. John had now saved enough money to start a small rancho, and with Sutter's help had obtained a land grant.

"At last you have your own land, John," said Sutter. "Will you leave soon for your rancho?"

"No," John replied, "I shall stay here and help you. We are far behind in all our work."

"But you came here to get your own land."

"I cannot leave now. I would be deserting a friend in need. I'll stay, Captain, until you find someone to take my place."

"Thank you, John. I'll try to hire someone to take over your duties," said Sutter. "But I'll never find anyone like you. You are my best—my trusted friend."

The busy days sped by. During the fall more than two hundred American settlers reached the fort. There were now almost eight hundred Americans in northern California.

The newly-arrived settlers were hungry and exhausted after their long trip across the plains and mountains. Sutter fed them all, gave jobs to those who wanted work, and helped others obtain land grants.

Among the Americans who took jobs at the fort were James Marshall, a jack-of-all-trades, and a New England schoolteacher, William Ide. Another man, Ezekiel Merritt, a rough, old trapper, set to work making and mending traps.

Most of the settlers were hard-working, rugged men of sterling character. There were some, however, who cared nothing for law and order.

It was not long before the Americans were in trouble with the proud, quick-tempered Californios. The Americans did not understand these carefree people and looked down upon them.

Sutter and John tried to tell the settlers that most of the Californios were fine honorable people. But the harm had been done. The bold manners of the thoughtless Americans offended the Californios. They came to believe that all Americans were greedy, land-hungry people and resented their growing strength in the country.

The rumors that Mexico and the United States were on the verge of war over Texas did not help matters. Texas had once belonged to Mexico, but, with the aid of its American settlers, had won its independence. In 1845, Texas was admitted to the United States. Almost at once a dispute with Mexico followed over the Texas boundary lines.

"The Americans intend to take over our country, too," said many Californios.

"Maybe that is why Lieutenant Frémont was out here a few years ago," others said. "He claimed he was on an exploring trip. But was he?"

The unrest steadily increased. Suspicion flared even higher when Frémont suddenly arrived in California. He was now a captain and he had a party of sixty well-armed men with him. He was on another exploring trip. This time he hoped to find a better route to Oregon.

Frémont remained at Sutter's Fort a few days and then left for Monterey. He called upon the military commander of California and asked for permission to explore the country.

The commander gave Frémont permission to explore the southeast. He warned Frémont not to travel through the settled valleys nearer the coast.

Frémont thanked the commander and was on his way. He led his sixty men straight through the forbidden valleys. The military commander was very angry. He sent a message to the young officer and ordered him to leave the country.

At first Frémont refused to leave. A few days later, however, he and his men headed northward for Oregon.

On the way the party stopped at Sutter's Fort. The settlers were disturbed when they learned why Frémont had been ordered to leave the country. Why, they asked one another, had he disobeyed the military commander?

"He must have some good reasons for his action," said William Ide.

"Sure he has," spoke up Ezekiel Merritt, the trapper who feared no man. "I'm standing by him."

"So am I," said another settler. "But it may mean trouble for all of us."

"We're headed for trouble anyway," said Merritt. "Frémont is the only one who can help us."

They went to Frémont and asked him to remain in California. He thanked them for their faith in him, but told them that he could not remain.

"If there is trouble will you come back and help us?" questioned a settler.

"I am a soldier," Frémont replied. "I shall carry out whatever orders I receive from my government. That is all I can promise you."

Although Frémont left California, he had stirred up plenty of trouble. The military commander begged the governor to prepare for a possible American invasion. The governor refused because he feared that the army would be used to remove him from power.

The bitter quarrels of the two leaders divided California when unity was desperately needed. A civil war seemed likely to break out any day.

Vallejo and other men of fine standing were alarmed. They were patriots and they loved their country. They compared their weak, unsteady government to the strong, stable government of the United States. They began to favor the American cause.

Watchful and anxious, the American settlers waited for something to happen. The almost daily crop of rumors added to their unrest. One day they heard that Mexico was going to sell California to England. The next day the news was that the governor was going to sell the country to France—or was it to Russia?

There was much loud talk on the part of some settlers. On the whole, however, the settlers were cautious. They did not want trouble. But they were determined not to be pushed around like cattle. No, sir! They were Americans and they could be pushed just so far and no farther!

It was the end of May, 1846, when the unrest of the settlers reached the breaking point. Frémont was back in California! Why had he returned? He would not tell except to say that he had received a letter from Washington.

The settlers welcomed Frémont's return with

open arms. The military commander and his followers were furious. They begged the governor to forget their old quarrels and rally to their country's cause. Again the governor refused.

Hastily the commander tried to whip his army into shape. He sent an officer with a party of soldiers northward to round up all the government-owned horses they could find. In a short time the soldiers had about one hundred fifty horses and were on their way back to Monterey.

The news leaked out that the horses were to be used in a civil war against the governor. Another rumor claimed that the horses were to be used against the American settlers.

"We have listened to enough threats," stormed Ezekiel Merritt. "Let's do something!"

"What can we do?" asked the settlers.

"Do! We can stop the soldiers and take the horses away from them," spoke up William Ide.

"We're in serious trouble!" shouted Merritt. "Come on, men. I want fifteen or twenty volunteers to follow me and get those horses."

Merritt's men surprised the soldiers and the

horses were captured without any trouble. Merritt sent the soldiers on to Monterey with a sharp message for their military commander.

The settlers drove the horses back to Frémont's camp and left them. Then joined by more volunteers, the party raced westward across the valley.

Late the same evening a group of Americans came to the fort. They entered the office where Sutter and John Bidwell were at work. The leader of the group told Sutter that Merritt's men were on their way to capture Sonoma.

"Sonoma!" John and Sutter exclaimed.

"Yes. They intend to make Vallejo a prisoner."

Sutter jumped to his feet. "He is a friend of the Americans. Does Frémont know about this?"

"He may, but we are not certain," answered the leader. "We did not go to his camp because we are not friendly with him."

"This is bad news. I fear it means war."

"Maybe you can prevent it," said a man.

"No one can stop it now," Sutter replied. "We must wait for news from Merritt."

"Captain," the leader asked, "in case of war will

you remain loyal to the Mexican government?"

"How can you question Captain Sutter's friendship and loyalty?" John asked angrily. "No one has done more for the Americans in California."

"You do not need to defend me, John," said Sutter quietly. "I'll let my actions speak for me." He turned to the men. "I am a Mexican citizen. My lands were given to me by Mexico. But I have always been a good friend to the Americans. I do not want war. I do not think it is necessary." He paused. "But I promise you that when the war begins you'll find me fighting on your side."

The following days were long, anxious ones. No word came from Merritt's men. It could not be possible that they had been defeated. Sonoma was not a defended town.

When General Vallejo had been the military commander of California, he had stationed soldiers in the old fort. But since he had been removed from power no troops had been posted there. Sonoma was now only a sleepy little town grown up around the adobe houses of Vallejo and his large family.

Late in the afternoon of June 15, Merritt and some of his men returned to Frémont's camp. With them were General Vallejo and three other important men from Sonoma. They were prisoners of war. The day before, at sunrise, the general had surrendered his little town to the Americans.

"We captured Sonoma without any trouble," boasted Merritt. "Bill Ide is now in command, and we have declared California a republic. We even made a flag. It's a fine flag with a big star and an old grizzly bear painted on it."

"A grizzly bear?" questioned a man.

"Yes, sir!" Merritt replied. "You know a grizzly bear stands and fights. And that's exactly what we intend to do."

"I'll fight for the republic," said a settler.

"So will I," spoke up another.

As others shouted their eagerness to join the fight, Merritt exclaimed, "Good! Be ready to leave for Sonoma with me in the morning. I just came back to turn the prisoners over to Frémont."

In the morning Merritt and his party left Frémont's camp. Frémont, with a party of soldiers guarding the prisoners, rode to Sutter's Fort.

Sutter and John were waiting for the young officer. They heard his quick footsteps in the hall.

"I wish to see you alone, Captain Sutter," Frémont said as he entered the room.

At a nod from Sutter, John left and closed the door behind him. Almost at once he was startled to hear the angry voices of the two men. A few minutes later the door opened and Frémont strode down the long hall and out into the square.

John hurried to Sutter's office. "Captain," he asked, "what is the matter?"

"Frémont ordered me to keep the prisoners locked up here at my fort. I told him I would carry out his orders, but that I felt we had no right to hold them unless the United States and Mexico were at war. He was angry. 'If you don't like what I am doing,' he said, 'you can join the Mexicans.' "

"It was a thoughtless remark," said John, "I am sure he didn't mean it."

"Maybe he didn't. But it shows clearly that he does not trust me. Maybe other Americans feel the same way."

"Indeed, they don't! They know you are a loyal friend." John paused. "Captain, I am leaving soon to fight for California. I want to say this before I go. In war, Frémont will win California for the United States. But you, in peace, paved the way for his victory. In peace you won the hearts of my countrymen."

Sutter turned quickly away. "Thank you, John," he said simply. Then he squared his shoulders and left to care for his prisoners.

Events moved swiftly. John, at Sonoma, helped draw up the constitution for the republic. He was made an officer in the army.

Word was received that the military commander of California and his troops were on the way to Sonoma. Bill Ide at once sent a rider to Frémont appealing to him to come to the aid of the Americans. As the rider dashed eastward the Bear Flag Army marched to meet the enemy.

Frémont was disturbed when the rider gave him the message. The young officer still did not know whether the United States and Mexico were at war. If he joined the fight and his country was at peace, then he would be severely punished.

But Frémont did not hesitate. He was a man of action. He was an American, and right or wrong his fellow-Americans were in danger. He rushed to their aid.

Frémont overtook the Americans. Then in command of the army he pursued the retreating enemy. He seized the little fort at San Francisco. He gave the beautiful bay its lovely and now famous name Golden Gate.

At last on July 10, Frémont received the news for which he had been waiting so long. The United States and Mexico were at war. The war, caused by the dispute in Texas, had begun in May.

The Bear Flag of the republic was hauled down. It had served its purpose. Up went the flag of the United States. From now on it would be the fighting banner of California.

John was ordered to carry the news to Sutter's Fort. He rode swiftly and reached the fort before dawn. At sunrise, as a cannon roared and the people cheered, Sutter raised the Stars and Stripes over his fort.

"I do not need to tell you, John," said Sutter "how happy I am today. And yet," he paused, "I feel a deep sense of sadness, too. We are at war and war is a terrible thing. Mexico cannot win. Her soldiers are poorly trained and badly equipped!"

"But they are brave," said John. "They will fight for the country they love."

"As soon as I settle my affairs at the fort, I shall offer my services to Frémont," said Sutter. He looked up at the new flag waving proudly in the breeze. "I must fight for my country—for I am now an American."

* * * *

The conquest of California was over in the fall of 1846. Mexico, however, did not give up its claim to California until the Mexican War ended in 1848. California then became a territory of the United States.

The Mill at Coloma

THE CHANGE OF FLAGS did not affect the native Californians very much. They were now under the control of a military governor of the United States instead of a Mexican governor. But that was almost the only difference. Life went on much as usual in the drowsy little towns and on the great ranches.

Life for the American settlers, however, took on new meaning. Now the golden, sunny land was truly theirs. From the fertile soil they would build the future greatness of their adopted homeland.

At Fort Sutter these were busy days. Sutter, always a hard worker, was busier than ever. He had hired a man to take over John's duties. But it was with John that Sutter discussed his plans for the future.

"The people in the East will soon learn that California is a territory of the United States," said Sutter. "I am certain that hundreds will come out here to settle."

"Yes," John agreed, "and every single one of them will head for your fort."

"I know," Sutter nodded. "I am doing all I can to be ready for them. I shall plant more wheat and buy more herds of cattle than ever before. I shall fill my storehouses with supplies. I'll have tools, guns, ammunition, traps, clothing, and everything they will need."

"It is like you to make plans to help the settlers. What would we do without you?"

Sutter held up his hand. "My greatest pleasure is to help others, John," he said. "I like to think that I am doing my share in making California a fine, strong state for our country." He paused a second and added, "I might need help myself someday. Maybe then the people I have helped will remember me."

"Of course they will!" John exclaimed. But the thought flashed through his mind that Sutter would never need help. Why, he owned more land than any other man in California—in all America!

He counted his cattle, horses, sheep, and hogs by the thousands. His stores brought in a great deal of money even though he did not charge the poor settlers for supplies.

Sutter was powerful, wealthy, and famous. But best of all he was beloved. His very name was the magic charm which led the settlers across the plains and mountains. Many times sturdy, bold settlers faltered along the way. But, weary and often starving, they pushed on. They knew that at the end of the long, long trail he would welcome them. He would not fail them.

"I have made my plans very carefully," Sutter continued. "The settlers won't start across the plains until next spring. They have to wait for the grass to grow so they can feed their animals on the trail. They should reach my fort in the fall. By that time the crops will be harvested and I'll have plenty of food supplies. But," he frowned, "there is one thing that worries me."

"What is it, Captain?"

"It will take a lot of flour to feed so many people," Sutter replied. "The method of grinding the grain by hand to make flour is too slow. I should have a flour mill. I need lumber to build a good flour mill. That means I must have a sawmill where I can cut the lumber. I have tried many times to locate a site for a sawmill, but I have not been successful. Something was always wrong. If there were enough trees then there was no stream to furnish the water power for the mill. If there was a stream then the trees were of such poor quality that they would not make good lumber."

"Yes, I know," said John. "I remember once when you sent Jim Marshall out to see if he could find a favorable spot."

"Jim is out now trying to find a site. If he finds one, we will go into the lumber business together. I'm not sure he will make a very good business partner. Jim is a queer sort of fellow."

"Yes, he is," John laughed a little as he remembered Marshall's gruff manners. "But he is a hard worker and he is honest."

"Indeed he is! And he is the best carpenter I ever had. He can make anything," Sutter replied.

"Now, I have talked about my plans long enough. What about you, John? What are you doing?"

"Well, for one thing, I sold my land grant. It was not what I really wanted. The land I intend to own someday is on Chico Creek. Two friends of mine own it now. But they have promised that if they sell it I will have a chance to buy it. That means that I must have the money ready."

"I will lend you the money you need, John."

"I know, Captain. But I still say that I'll make my own way here in the West. I can earn the money I need by locating land for other settlers."

"You're right, John. The settlers need someone who can survey the country and mark the boundary lines. They trust you because they know you will draw up their claims correctly."

"I'll be very careful," said John. "I don't want them to have any trouble with claim jumpers. I'll never forget that old rascal who jumped my land in Missouri. But," he added quickly, "if he hadn't I might not have come to California. Now I am glad, for this is the land of opportunity."

"Yes," Sutter agreed, "and the best years are

just ahead of us." He was silent a while and then in an almost impatient tone of voice he asked, "Why doesn't Marshall let me know something? There is so much to do and so little time."

A few days later Jim Marshall returned with good news. He had found a favorable place in the mountains near Coloma to erect the sawmill. It was on the South Fork of the American River, about forty-five miles from the fort.

"We're in luck this time," Marshall reported. "The pine trees in the forests will make good lumber. The water in the South Fork is swift. That means we will have all the water power we need."

"It's too good to be true!" exclaimed Sutter.

"I'll start building the mill right away, and it will be a good one," said Marshall. The excitement of his good fortune had changed him. He was cheerful and full of plans. "I'll get the tools and provisions I need and hurry back to Coloma."

"I'll go with you," said Sutter.

"Fine! Fine!" Marshall turned to John. "Why don't you join us?"

"Thanks, Jim, but I have some work of my own to do. I'll come a little later."

"Come any time. I'll be glad to see you."

John didn't have a chance to visit Marshall until December. All fall he had been kept busy locating land claims for the settlers. But at last he was on his way to Coloma.

The trip to the mountain valley was difficult. The road was rough and in places hardly more than a path. It wound its way ever higher through a rugged country of steep hills and deep canyons.

Marshall was glad to see John, and proudly showed him the new sawmill. It was almost completed except for the millrace, or channel, in which the water of the Fork would flow to the mill wheel. It was this swift current of water that would turn the big wheel to furnish the power for the sawmill.

"Jim, you have done a fine job," praised John. "How long will it take to dig the millrace?"

"Not more than a few weeks," Marshall answered. "Then we'll be ready to set the wheel in place. It's a tricky job to set the wheel in the millrace. If the wheel is set too low we'll have to dig the millrace deeper."

"I hope you won't be delayed, Jim."

"So do I," Marshall replied as he rubbed a hard hand across the stubby beard on his chin. "I want to get started in this lumber business as soon as I can. You know, Bidwell, this is the first chance I've ever really had to make something of myself. I'm going to work very hard to succeed."

"I wish you all the luck in the world, Jim, all the luck in the world."

John stayed at Coloma a week. Each morning he worked with the men who were chopping down trees. In the afternoons he explored the mountain streams and followed old Indian trails through the canyons.

After saying good-by to Marshall and his workmen, John returned to his own job. Now and then he thought of Marshall and wondered if the sawmill had been completed.

While John was mapping out claims in the north he visited his friends on Chico Creek. He rode with them over their fine ranch, and longed for the day when he could buy the land from them. One friend offered to share a part of his ranch with John. John quickly accepted the generous offer.

John bought a herd of cattle and hired some Indians to work for him. Fields were plowed and wheat and other grains were planted.

John also wished to start an orchard. To purchase the best trees meant a trip to the coast. Since he wanted only the best trees he left at once. He bought a large stock of young fruit trees and ordered them shipped by boat up the Sacramento River to his ranch.

On the return trip John stopped at Sutter's Fort. It was late at night when he arrived, but a light was still burning in Sutter's office. While an Indian took care of his horse, John hurried to the big house. He entered the house and strode down the familiar hall. He knocked on the heavy door of the office.

"Come in," Sutter called. "Oh, I'm glad to see you!" he exclaimed as John entered. He rose quickly to his feet, and in his haste upset the chair at his desk. As he rushed across the room, he repeated, "Oh, I am glad to see you!"

"And I am glad to be here, Captain," John replied. He was, however, a little puzzled. They always greeted each other with great pleasure for they were real friends. But tonight John sensed that something was wrong. Had something happened at the sawmill?

"What is the matter, Captain?" he asked. "Has Marshall—"

"Who told you?" interrupted Sutter. "Who told you the secret?"

"What secret?" questioned John.

"Didn't you come from the mill?"

"No, Captain."

Sutter looked for a long minute into John's eyes. Then he turned, walked slowly back to his desk and sat down in his chair. He motioned for John to sit down in a chair beside him.

Without a word Sutter unlocked a drawer in the desk and opened it. He reached inside and held up a small box. His hands trembled as he gave it to John.

John lifted the cover of the box. Inside were three small pieces of yellow metal. He turned the box over and spilled the pieces into the palm of his hand. The largest piece was about the size of a pea. He rubbed it between his fingers.

"It looks like gold," he said glancing at Sutter.

"It is gold, John—pure gold!"

"Gold!"

Sutter nodded.

"Where did you get it? When? How?"

Sutter leaned across the desk. "I haven't dared tell anyone," he said. "But I trust you, John. I must talk to you."

"Why, of course, Captain."

"Jim Marshall has discovered gold at the sawmill."

"He has!" John exclaimed.

"Yes, it happened this way," Sutter continued. "The mill wheel was set too low. The race had to be dug a little deeper. Jim had the men work during the days. At night he would let the water run through the race to carry away the loose dirt.

"On the morning of January 24, about two weeks

ago, he was examining the race. On the bottom of the race he saw something shining in the clear water. He stopped and picked up two small pieces of yellow metal. At first he thought it was gold, but he was not sure because all the gold he had ever seen was reddish in color."

Sutter paused and shook his head. "Marshall showed the metal to his workmen," he went on. "He told them that he thought it was gold. They laughed at him and said he was crazy. Nevertheless, while they worked in the race they kept looking for the metal. They found three more ounces, and then Marshall came to the fort.

"I'll never forget that cold, rainy night, John. Marshall was like a wild man. He burst into my office and locked the door. He pushed a chest against the door so no one, he said, could enter to spy upon us. Then he gave me the yellow metal he had found. I can still hear him ask over and over, 'Is it gold, Captain? Is it gold?' I told him I didn't know, but that I would test it with an acid. I did, and it was gold—pure gold."

"I can hardly believe it," said John.

"At first Marshall couldn't believe it either. But when he did he wanted me to go back to the mill with him that night. I told him it would be wiser to wait until morning and that I would then go with him. He refused to remain. He left in a downpour of rain."

"Did you go to the mill the next day?"

"Yes, a party of men and I left at sunrise," answered Sutter. "On the way we found Marshall lying in the road. He had fallen from his horse and was too ill to get to the mill. We had to travel slowly for a man had to hold Marshall on his horse.

"But bright and early the next morning he was on the job. We examined the race. I found the three pieces of gold which I showed you. Many of the workmen had found gold, too."

Sutter threw up his hands. "They all wanted to quit work and search for gold. I begged them not to quit. I pleaded with them to keep the discovery of gold a secret—at least until the mill was finished. They finally promised and agreed to go back to work."

"Will they stay on the job?" asked John.

"I don't know what will happen up there," answered Sutter. "But I do know this. A rush for gold could ruin me. It could mean the end of everything I have worked for all these years. It could mean the end of all my dreams."

"How could it, Captain? The gold on your property belongs to you."

"Do you think the gold seekers will respect my rights to the property? Oh no, John. Gold makes men lawless and selfish."

"But you have done so much for them, and for California. Surely the people will remember."

"Gold," replied Sutter, "holds a strange power over men. They will forget me."

He rose from his chair and began to pace back and forth. Suddenly he stopped. "Whatever happens they shall not take my land from me," he cried. "New Helvetia is mine!"

Pay Dirt

JIM MARSHALL was not the first man to discover gold in California. Other men had also found the precious metal. Their discoveries revealed only small amounts of gold and, therefore, had caused little excitement. But at Coloma there seemed to be no end to the gold supply.

Gold! Gold! It was everywhere!

Marshall's workmen found flakes of gold in the river and streams rushing down from the mountains. Gold dust, fine and crumbly, and sand-like grains of gold were found in the ravines and gulches.

One man, digging in the gravel on a hillside, picked up a nugget as big as his thumb. His shouts of excitement brought the others rushing to him. The sand and gravel flew in all directions as the men dug with their pocketknives to unearth more of the treasure.

Marshall was greatly worried. One by one his workmen quit. The unfinished mill stood deserted.

Within a few weeks the great discovery leaked out. The news spread slowly, for communication was poor and the towns and ranches far apart.

At first the people paid little attention to the gold stories. That is, the steadier, more sober-minded men refused to believe the reports. They remembered the other discoveries, and this time they decided they would not rush off to search for gold. They would wait.

Some men, however, decided to go to Coloma and see for themselves if the reports were true. When they returned a few weeks later all caution was thrown to the winds. The men had come back with heavy bags of gold and endless stories of the great wealth of the gold fields.

The rush for gold had begun!

Ranchmen left their herds of cattle and farmers left their crops. Storekeepers closed their stores and shops. Clerks, cooks, preachers, lawyers, and teachers gave up their jobs. Sailors deserted their ships. Convicts broke out of jail

To a man they headed for Coloma. They rode horses or mules. Some walked. Others traveled in wagons or carts.

John and Sutter were with Marshall at Coloma when the first large party of gold seekers arrived. Silently they watched the new arrivals unpack their supplies. And then, although it was late in the afternoon, the gold-hungry men hurried down to the river.

"Why did this happen to me?" Marshall lashed out in anger. "Why?"

"I keep asking myself the same question," said Sutter in a low voice.

"I should have known better than to have gone into business with you," Marshall shouted. "This is all your fault."

"Why, Jim," spoke up John, "you don't know what you are saying. Surely you don't believe—"

"I don't know what to believe any more," broke in Marshall. The anger had gone out of his voice. He was a broken, helpless man. "I don't care what happens to Sutter, to you—to anyone. All I care about is my mill. And now it will never be finished."

He turned and half-walked, half-stumbled to his silent mill. There alone in the shadows he stood with bowed head—the man who had discovered gold.

"Poor old Jim," said Sutter.

"I am sorry for him, too," John replied, "but I am worried about you, Captain. What is happening at your fort?"

"Well, some of my best men have already quit. Others have told me that as soon as the crops are harvested they intend to leave, too."

"I'll come back and work for you."

"I know you would, John, but there isn't very much that you or anyone else can do until the rush for gold is over."

"I'll do anything to help you," insisted John. "I owe you a debt I can never repay."

"You paid me back a long time ago, my friend. Now you must think of yourself and your future."

"What do you advise me to do?" asked John.

"Dig your share of this gold," answered Sutter, "and get out before you lose it all. Buy the land you want on Chico Creek and settle down."

"That is exactly what I intend to do."

"Then do it, John. Let me give you some more advice. Make up your own party of men you can trust. But don't search for gold around Coloma."

"Why not, Captain?"

"All the gold seekers will come here," replied Sutter. "Go to some other mountain river where you won't be bothered. If you don't find gold you can always come back here."

"I could go to the Feather River," said John. "I know the Feather fairly well. When I worked at Hock Farm I often explored the land along the river."

Following Sutter's advice John talked over his plans with four good friends. The men were eager to go with him. Without delay they purchased their supplies and set out to find their fortunes.

The men had little trouble finding "color," as traces of gold were called, in the Feather River. But at the end of a day of hard work they were disappointed. They had only a small amount of gold dust and flakes.

They broke camp and rode farther upstream to

prospect for gold. Again they were disappointed and again they moved on.

Day after day it was the same old story. To be sure, they always found the color, but only in small amounts. They remembered the wealth of the Coloma gold fields and became discouraged.

"There must be plenty of gold up here somewhere or we wouldn't find the color," said John.

"I agree with you, John," spoke up one of the men. "But I can't understand why we find only dust and flakes."

"I can't understand it either," John replied. "Maybe it is because the dust and flakes are light in weight and are easily washed downstream. If that is true, then the heavier pieces of gold would remain near the foothills where the river comes down from the Sierra Nevada Mountains."

"By jingo!" exclaimed the man, "I think you're right."

"Then why don't we head for the foothills?"

"It will be just a waste of time," spoke up a man. "I'm for heading back to Coloma. I'm sorry, John," he added, "but I am discouraged."

"I am discouraged, too," John smiled a little. "Nevertheless, I am going on up the Feather."

The friends talked for some time. At last two men decided to return to Coloma. John and the other two men decided to go on. They said good-by to one another and parted with friendly wishes of good luck.

The trip up the lovely Feather was through a land of rugged beauty. Pine trees, straight and tall, covered the canyon walls. Deep ravines cut across the narrow winding path, making John and his friends travel far out of their way. Little streams tumbled down from the higher hills and raced on to join the Feather. Now and then the soft colors of the rainbow were caught in the mist of a waterfall.

When the men reached the foothills of the Sierra Nevadas they made camp. They rolled up in their blankets early that night for they wanted to start work at dawn.

In the morning after breakfast, each man struck out for himself. John was last to leave for it was his turn to attend to the few camp duties. He

watered the horses and mules in the river. Then he hobbled them where they could graze on fresh, green grass. He put out the breakfast campfire, being sure that no sparks remained in the ashes.

Whistling an old Spanish tune he made ready for the day's work. He touched his belt and felt to be sure that his pistol and a short, sturdy knife were in place.

He gathered up his mining tools and strode from camp. In one hand he carried a light pick and shovel and in the other a shallow iron pan.

He walked quickly along the bank of the Feather, staying close to the water's edge. At a point where a sand bar had formed in the river he stopped. He studied the sand more carefully.

"I'll try my luck here," he said dropping his shovel and pan. He loosened the sand with the sharp-pointed pick. Then he squatted on the bank and reached for the pan. He scooped up a pan full of sand, some gravel, thick mud, and water.

He held the pan in both hands and moved it slowly in a circle. With each turn a little of the watery mixture spilled over the sloping sides of the pan. When most of the water was gone he dipped the pan into the stream and refilled it with water. Then slowly, carefully he moved the pan in a circle to pour off the mixture.

It was a slow process. The miners called it panning for gold. It was, however, an almost foolproof method because if plenty of water was used the gold could not be poured off with the sand and gravel. Since the gold was heavier than the sand it sank to the bottom of the pan.

The process was repeated until only about a handful of the mixture remained in the pan. If the miner was lucky the dirt mixture contained gold dust, flakes, or nuggets. When gold was found in the mixture it was called pay dirt.

John found no color in the dirt. He tucked the legs of his trousers deeper into his heavy boots and waded out into the stream. He scooped up another pan full of what he hoped would be pay dirt. Again he squatted on the bank and slowly, carefully panned for gold.

"It's only dirt," he said throwing the mixture

away. He picked up his tools and walked on.

John worked steadily all morning. Once in a while he stood erect and stretched, for the squatting position made his muscles tired. The icy-cold water chilled him. The hot July sun beat down upon him. But he paid little attention to the discomforts. They were a part of a miner's life.

At noon his friends returned to camp. They called to him to join them for the noonday meal.

He bent over the pan again. "I'll be there as soon as I pan out," he called. He stirred the mixture with one hand and picked out a round, smooth piece of gravel. He was about to toss it away. Suddenly he realized that it was heavy—too heavy for a piece of gravel. It was gold!

He dropped the pan and jumped to his feet. "Boys, I— I—" he tried to shout.

He started running toward the camp. In his haste he stumbled over a rock. As he fell the nugget slipped from his hand and rolled into a ditch.

John scrambled to his feet and looked into the ditch. The bottom was covered with hundreds of small pebbles and larger pieces of gravel.

His heart sank, and the wild excitement of his discovery died within him. How could he find the nugget of gold again?

Stepping carefully so as not to disturb the stones John made his way into the ditch. He picked up a round, smooth piece of gravel. He held it for a second, testing its weight and then threw it away. He picked up another, another, and another.

"I know it's here," he said to himself reaching for a handful of gravel. "I saw it roll in."

He tested each stone before he threw it away. As he tested the last one his heart began to pound. His temples throbbed. It was not the first nugget he had found. This one was larger and more yellow.

"It's gold, but it isn't the one I lost," he whispered the words. He turned the nugget over and over in his hand.

He whipped the pistol from his belt. "Gold! Gold!" he shouted as he fired a shot into the air.

"John! John!" The men raced toward him. Laughing and talking all at the same time, the three friends examined the large nugget of gold.

"It's heavy!" exclaimed John. "It must be worth about five hundred dollars."

"Oh, more than that!" one friend exclaimed. "You'll get at least seven hundred dollars for it."

John untied the blue handkerchief he wore around his neck. He wrapped the nugget in the handkerchief and put them in the pocket of his flannel shirt. As he buttoned the flap on the pocket he said, "We're in luck, boys. This is pay dirt. Let's get busy."

The noonday meal was forgotten. All afternoon the men worked in the ditches along the river. Hour after hour they squatted at the water's edge and panned for gold. When it was too dark to see any longer they returned to camp.

Later, after supper, they sat around their blazing campfire. They were dog-tired, their muscles ached, but they were still too excited to go to sleep.

"There is as much gold up here as there is at Coloma," said one man. "By jingo, I'm glad I didn't go back."

"We have struck a rich bar of gold, all right," agreed John.

"You found it," said the second man. "It's your bar—Bidwell's Bar."

"No," laughed John. "We are friends and we stuck together."

The bar was even richer than John and his friends had dared hope it would be. Day after day they continued to pan out gold.

In October, when the rainy season began, the mining was over for the year. The men loaded their pack mules with supplies and bags of golden treasure. Then making plans to return in the spring, the lighthearted miners headed down the homeward trail for Chico Creek.

As always, John thrilled to the beauty of the fertile valley. He was pleased to have panned out enough gold to buy half the ranch. It was exciting to prospect for gold, he admitted. But he knew that nothing could ever change his deep, steady love for the rich land. He was glad. He was home again.

The Forty-niners

GOLD! Gold in California! The news spread across the nation. Ships carried the reports on to Europe, to China, to the far countries of the world.

In the United States true and false stories spread with equal speed. Daily the excitement increased, until the people talked of little else. With all the talk, however, there was a certain amount of caution. Was the news official? In December they would know.

President James K. Polk would then make the last report of his administration to Congress. Eagerly the people waited for the President's message.

Tuesday, December 5, 1848, the long-awaited message was delivered. The news was true and it was official. The President had spoken. Almost a year had passed since Jim Marshall had discovered gold at Coloma.

The country went wild. It was as though a madness had seized the people. Men made ready to leave at once for the gold fields. A few planned to take their families. But most of the men decided to go without their families. They planned to return to their homes after they had mined enough gold to make them wealthy.

The rush for gold was on!

Hundreds of men, living in the East and in the southern states, hurried to the nearest seaports. Docks were piled high with baggage addressed simply to Sutter's Fort. The gold seekers crowded aboard the ships. The first of the forty-niners were on their way.

Week after week the seaports were packed with hundreds and hundreds of men. They fought one another for passage. Transportation rates rose to the sky. Always there were plenty of men willing to pay the high prices. Many paid as high as a thousand dollars for a ticket besides signing up to work for nothing on board ship.

Most of the ships leaving the eastern ports followed the longest route to the land of gold. They sailed down the Atlantic Ocean to Cape Horn, the southernmost point of South America. Then, rounding the Horn, the ships entered the Pacific Ocean and sailed northward for California.

The long, long trip of seventeen thousand miles often took about nine months. The safeness of the route, however, made up for the great distance and the many months of travel.

The gold seekers who left from the southern ports usually followed a much shorter route. But it was a very difficult one.

Their ships sailed for the Isthmus of Panama. Landing on the Atlantic side the people had to make their way across the jungle country to the Pacific port. Although the trip across the Isthmus was only about sixty miles, it was filled with hardships.

Few people had shelters of any kind. Few had enough food. Scores died from disease. Many were robbed and murdered. Then once at the Pacific port the gold seekers had to wait, sometimes for weeks, for a boat to take them on to California.

By March, seventeen thousand forty-niners were

on the ocean routes bound for California. But this record was to be broken by the people of the middle states. They had to wait until spring. But when they started—man alive—there was no holding them! In less than one month eighteen thousand were heading west for California. They had their own route, the Overland Route. Theirs was the trail of the covered wagon.

Two well-known starting points were the frontier trading-post towns of Independence and St. Joseph, Missouri. During the spring, so many wagon trains left that the people in the towns no longer watched them depart. Only the small boys still thrilled to the now familiar take-off.

It was always exciting to watch the captain inspect the wagons of his train and hear him shout his orders to the drivers. It was fun to see the drivers snap their long whips out over the heads of their oxen, mule, or horse teams. Wagons creaked and groaned as they rolled down the streets and headed for the western trails. The take-off was always noisy, but to the boys it was a song of high adventure.

The men of the covered wagons would have agreed with the boys. It was adventure—plus plenty of hard work. Traveling across the plains had not changed since the Bidwell party had blazed the way in 1841.

There were the same long miles of prairies to be crossed, streams to be forded, and roads to be built. There were the sudden downpours of rain, and the hours wasted when the wagons were stuck in the deep mud. Then there were days when the dust was so thick it choked both men and animals. There were the same weary, endless miles of sand and sagebrush. There was the blazing heat of the sun. There were the cold winds of the mountain passes.

Few of the men had been beyond the frontier settlements. Their lack of knowledge and experience on the trail made them suffer many unnecessary hardships. Fortunately the Indians caused little trouble. The reason for this was that the white men were traveling through and not staying in the Indian country.

There were other enemies, however, even more

terrible than the Indians. Hunger, thirst, and disease! Thousands died on the way.

But the stronger pushed on. In sharing the same hardships the men became good friends. They were sturdy fellows and they had a way of laughing at their troubles.

When the going was toughest someone would begin to sing. One by one the others would join him. Somehow the song brought hope and comfort. The miles ahead seemed less long, the hardships less trying.

At night in camp there was music, for always some man had brought along an old banjo or fiddle. The weary men gathered around the campfire to sing the old, familiar songs of home and loved ones. Then to hide their lonely, homesick hearts they called for gay songs of nonsense and good cheer.

As the flames of the campfire died down they would sing one last song. It was a new one of Stephen Foster's, and this one was their favorite. The music had a swing to it and the words—well, the forty-niners had changed the words. They had made it their own song, their theme song.

"I'm going to Californy
The gold dust for to see.
It rained all night the day I left.
The weather, it was dry.
The sun so hot I froze to death.
Oh, brother, don't you cry.

Oh, Californy!
That's the land for me!
I'm bound for Sacramento
With a washbowl on my knee."

A song of nonsense? Yes, but it was sung by strong, brave men, and it helped them overcome the hardships of the western trails.

But at last by land and by sea the forty-niners finally reached California. Those who came by sea landed at San Francisco. In the beautiful Golden Gate harbor, hundreds of deserted ships rode at anchor, their crews off to the gold fields.

The new arrivals did not remain long in the rapidly growing city of tents, wooden shacks, and dusty streets. They went on up the Sacramento

River to Fort Sutter. Here at the fort they met the men who had followed the trails of the covered wagons.

At Fort Sutter the full effect of the rush for gold could be seen. The famous old fort was a beehive of activity. Stores and shops were crowded with mobs of red-shirted, bearded forty-niners.

The prices they paid for tools, clothing, and other supplies were sky high. The goods were expensive because everything had to be brought in by boat. Sutter no longer produced anything at the fort as his workmen were gold seekers, too.

The men wasted little time at the fort. They bought their supplies and scattered to the diggings as the miners called the gold fields.

Coloma was still the favorite mining camp. But other diggings were coming into their own. There was Hangtown, some eight miles south, and Weber's Creek, Cedar Ravine, Deer Creek Diggings, Bidwell's Bar, and dozens of others.

The diggings were scattered along the rivers and streams. Each had its own camp of rude shelters and tents. Little was done to make the camp attractive or even comfortable. Why waste the time? The faintest rumor that richer diggings had been discovered near by was enough to send the miners rushing to the new place. Like a mushroom, the new camp sprang up over night. The old deserted camp became a ghost town.

The gold seekers usually rushed to the nearest diggings. Some, however, headed northward along the Feather River for Bidwell's Bar.

It was in September when the first party of forty-niners was on its way to the bar. One night, shortly before dark, the men made camp off the trail. While they were cooking supper over the blazing campfire they heard the jingle of bells.

The sound of the bells came nearer. At last a pack train of mules appeared on the winding trail. In the lead rode a tall, black-haired man.

The easy manner in which the man rode made one of the miners say, "He must be a Mexican. I hear they are the best horsemen in the world."

"Maybe he owns one of those great ranches," spoke up another forty-niner.

"Hello," the rider called waving his big hat.

The party of miners looked at one another.

"He's an American," said one quickly.

"Hello! Hello!" they shouted.

The rider waved his hat again and turned in his saddle. He called an order to the drivers of the pack train. Then touching his mule lightly, he raced toward the men. As he joined them he reined in his mule and swung from the saddle.

"I'm John Bidwell," he said.

"Bidwell—of Bidwell's Bar!" the men exclaimed.

"Yes."

"What luck to meet you," said a man. "We're on our way to your bar."

"Well," John laughed, "it's hardly my bar."

"Is there plenty of gold up there?"

"There certainly is."

"Why don't you spend the night with us?"

"I'd like to very much," replied John.

By now the pack train had reached the camp. The jingle of bells stopped as the first driver halted the lead mule of the train. The other drivers halted their animals, too.

"Make camp," John called to the leader.

"The bells are a very pretty ornament," said a forty-niner. He pointed to the arch of bells hung over the neck of the lead mule. "I guess I'll get some for my mule. Maybe with music the old fellow will step along a little faster."

John laughed. "I like the music of the bells, too," he said. "But that is not the reason we use them. They are a warning to others on the trail. The mountain paths are so narrow in places that if you meet someone you can't pass."

"Oh, I understand," said the man. "When you hear the bells it's a warning to wait at a wider place on the trail until the party passes you."

"That's right," John replied.

After the drivers unloaded the mules and watered and hobbled them for the night they joined the men at the campfire. Talking and laughing the group cooked and ate the evening meal.

John and the drivers asked many questions about life in the States. The forty-niners, more interested in the gold fields, asked endless questions about mining.

John told them how he had found gold at the bar and how a little camp had grown up there since the discovery. He told that many of the men were panning out more than two hundred dollars' worth of gold each day.

"Is that all!" a forty-niner exclaimed. "Why at Sutter's Fort I heard that you could pick up a thousand dollars' worth of gold every day."

"I'm afraid that you'll hear many stories that are not true," John replied.

"How much gold do you find?"

"Well," John answered, "some days when I'm lucky I pan out several hundred dollars' worth of gold. Other days I have found only a few ounces of dust and flakes. And," he laughed a little, "there have been days when I didn't even find color."

"We should have gone to Coloma," the man said, turning to his friends.

"We'll be lucky," one replied. "We'll strike it rich at the bar."

"Sure we will," the others agreed.

The man turned again to John and asked, "Why

aren't you panning for gold if there is so much pay dirt at the bar?"

"That's a fair enough question," John smiled. "And I don't blame you for asking it. I spend very little time panning for gold now. I have other interests. I have a ranch a few miles northwest of the bar. I spend a few days each week at the ranch to direct my Indian workmen."

"And he owns a trading post at the bar, too," spoke up a driver of the pack train. "We bring up food and other supplies from Fort Sutter to the miners."

"I don't understand it at all," said a forty-niner as he shook his head. "I've come all the way from Ohio to mine for gold. And here you are, Bidwell, living in California and yet you spend only a part of your time in the diggings."

"Mining isn't the only way to make money out here," John explained. "The rush for gold is developing many new industries."

"Maybe you're right, but I wouldn't be a businessman. Why, in one day I might pan out more gold than you could make in a year."

"That's true," agreed John with a laugh.

The men talked until late that night. But at dawn they were on the trail. Since the pack train traveled more slowly, the forty-niners rode on ahead.

"We'll see you at the bar," they called.

John waved his hat in reply.

In the afternoon the pack train reached the bar. The party of forty-niners were already at work in the river. They remained bent over their pans, but the old-timers who needed new supplies ran to the trading post.

"Did you bring my blankets?" one called.

"Did you bring a shovel for me?" another asked.

"Beans! Beans! Beans!" laughed a miner as he kicked a heavy pack with the toe of his muddy, wet boot. "Didn't you get some fresh vegetables this time, Bidwell?" he asked turning to John.

"Yes, I was lucky to get several packs of onions, and turnips, and some potatoes."

"Whoopee!" the men shouted. "No beans for supper tonight."

The men helped unload the packs, and the trading began. There were blankets, tools, red flannel shirts, trousers, and boots. Packs of beans, salt pork, and flour were opened. The miners used the flour to make a sort of bread that was called, sour dough. These three items of food made up the daily fare for the men. No wonder they shouted when the fresh vegetables were unloaded.

The men paid John for the supplies with gold dust and flakes. A small scale was used to weigh out the gold. One man was showing John a large nugget when the forty-niners joined them.

"How much is it worth?" a forty-niner asked, pointing to the nugget.

John placed the piece of gold on the scale. He weighed it carefully. "You're in luck," he said handing the nugget back to the miner. "It's worth at least a thousand dollars."

"A thousand dollars!" the forty-niners exclaimed.

"Yes sir, at least that much." John grinned. "And boys, that's a lot more than I made today."

Bidwell's Bar

THE FORTY-NINERS lost no time in pitching their tents. The bar, they agreed was the place to strike it rich.

At the end of a week, however, the men were less sure. Each day from dawn to darkness they had dug, shoveled, and panned for gold. The few ounces of dust and flakes they had panned out were, they felt, poor reward for the hard work.

"We should have gone to Coloma or to some other diggings," said one man in disgust.

"Our luck will change," another insisted. "It's bound to change for the better."

"For the better! That's a good one. If it changes at all, it would have to be for the better. Our luck couldn't get any worse!"

While the men were talking, Bidwell joined them. Quickly they turned to him and asked him what to do.

"If I had come all the way to California to mine for gold I would not give up in one week," he answered. "I know you are discouraged and tired, but this is not the time to quit. Keep on the—"

"That's all very well for you to say," interrupted a man. "You are in luck. We haven't panned out enough gold to buy a bag of beans."

"Don't worry about your food supplies," said John. "I'll grubstake you to everything you need at the post." He paused for a moment and with a smile added, "I need more men to drive my pack mules. If you want a steady job with good pay, I'll be glad to hire you."

The forty-niners looked at one another.

At last a man said, "I didn't come out here to work for someone. I'm here to dig for gold, make some money, and then return to my wife and children. Although I haven't had any luck I keep thinking that the next pan may be pay dirt."

"That's the way I feel about it, too," said another.

John laughed softly. "Now you are talking like old-timers. When they are down-and-out they count on the next pan to change their luck."

The forty-niners went back to work. Their bad luck continued, but they stayed on the job. All they talked about was the next pan—the next—the next.

Then one morning the man who wanted to go to Coloma struck pay dirt. From a single pan he washed out more than fifteen hundred dollars' worth of gold.

Cheered by the good fortune of their companion, the others doubled their efforts. Before the rainy season began, each man had panned out several thousand dollars' worth of gold.

With the first fall rains, some of the miners returned to the settlements. The rest worked on until the cold rains became too severe to mine any longer. Packing their tools and bags of golden treasure they broke camp and left the bar.

The men headed southward for Sutter's Fort or for the little town of Sacramento growing up near by along the Sacramento River. Many, however, had already decided to go on to San Francisco. After months of hard work in the diggings they wanted to celebrate. They had plenty of gold. Why not spend it!

The last party to leave the bar rode with Bidwell to his ranch. As the men followed the winding trail they talked and laughed like old friends.

Then one man began to talk about his family, and a silence fell over the group.

"This gold-mining business is all right," the man said. "But I'm homesick and I don't care who knows it." He brushed the tears from his eyes with a hard, rough hand. "My wife and little girl and boy promised to write to me every week. What I wouldn't give to have their letters!"

"I like California," said another. "I am going to stay here. As soon as I make enough money I'll send for my family."

"That's a crazy thing to do!" exclaimed the men.

"Oh no, it isn't," said John. "California is a land of opportunity."

"It is right now," a man agreed. "But when the gold rush is over, what will happen?"

Before John could answer a man replied,

"Everyone will return to the States. California will be just the way it was before gold was discovered."

"Don't you believe it," said John quickly. "California will never be the same again. This is no longer a sleepy land belonging to Mexico. This is American territory, and already we are making plans to become a state in the Union."

"A state!"

"Yes, a state. And we have the men out here who will make it a great one."

"Who?"

"You," John answered, "you, the forty-niners."

The men sat a little straighter in their saddles. Why, it was true! The forty-niners had changed everything.

"During this year, 1849," John continued, "the population of California has jumped from less than twenty thousand people to almost a hundred thousand. Most of the gold seekers are from the United States. But men from England, Russia, France, and Germany are here, too. There are men from South America, Mexico, China, and from many other nations all over the world.

"The great increase in population has created many problems. Men must eat. They need clothing, shelter, and other supplies. California is not able to meet these sudden demands caused by the gold rush. The goods must be brought to us. We are far from the markets of the world.

"But shrewd businessmen in the East and in other countries are helping us. They are building bigger and faster ships. One eastern firm has almost completed a clipper ship. The new ship will cut the sailing time around the Horn to about three months."

"It can't be done!" a man exclaimed. "I came around the Horn, and the trip took nine months."

"Ho! Ho!" laughed another. "You don't know these Yankee shipbuilders. If faster ships are needed, they will build them."

"You may be right," the man replied. "But what happens after the ships are in port? It takes weeks to get the supplies delivered to the mining camps. Are the businessmen in the East going to solve that problem, too?"

"No, of course not," John answered. "We can handle that problem ourselves. It will take time to change from the old, slow methods of transportation to newer, faster methods. But it must be done. Mule pack trains and clumsy oxcarts must give way to wagons and stagecoaches. Trails and paths must be made into roads."

"The gold rush may be over before all this can be done," spoke up a man.

"I hope it will be," said John. "Then we can settle down to the real business of making California one of the great states in the Union."

"We'll do our share," the forty-niners promised.

Most of the gold seekers, however, had little or no interest in the future of California. But men like Bidwell, Sutter, Vallejo, and other old-timers were sincere in their love for California. They won the support of many forty-niners.

It was not an easy task, for among the miners were men from every walk of life. There were good men and bad, educated and uneducated, wealthy and poor. There were strong, brave men and there were robbers and crooks and gamblers.

But in spite of the difficulties, the better class of citizens continued to plan for statehood. A governor, senators, and other officials were elected. San Jose was chosen as the first capital of the would-be state.

In December, when the legislature met, the military governor resigned. With sincere wishes of good luck he turned over his duties to the forty-niner governor.

At once the new governor and the legislature went to work. Three important members of the senate were Sutter, Vallejo, and Bidwell—a Swiss, a Mexican, and an American.

A constitution was adopted. Sutter was given the honor of being the first man to sign it. Outside the hall thirty-one cannon boomed a salute. California was telling the world that soon the thirty-first star would be added to the flag of the United States.

When the legislature adjourned John and Sutter took a boat to San Francisco. They had business to attend to in the port city before returning to their homes. They also wanted to spend some time together for the busy days at the meeting had given them little chance to visit together.

As their ship sailed northward, the two men stood at the rail. Now and then John glanced at Sutter, but he was careful not to let his friend know that he was worried about him. Sutter had changed. He had grown old. His hair had turned white. The deep, tired lines in his face told of sleepless nights. He was thinner, and he no longer held himself proudly erect.

John, remembering the gracious, smiling Sutter of other days, was sad. "The gold rush," he said to himself, "has done this to him." Gently he placed a hand on his friend's shoulder.

Sutter drew a deep breath. "The odds are against me, John," he said in a low voice. "But I'm still fighting. I have rented the fort to some traders and have moved to Hock Farm. Maybe there with my faithful Indians I can hang on until the gold rush is over."

"I thought you were making thousands of dollars by selling supplies to the miners. Every time I have been there the stores were crowded."

"My clerks were not honest," explained Sutter. "They cheated me out of thousands and thousands of dollars. But that isn't all, John. I am having trouble with the forty-niners. Now, most of the miners are fine men." He brought a fist down on the deck rail. "I do not blame them for what is happening to me. But many of the men have no respect for another's property."

Sutter threw up his hands, "These lawless men! They take what they want—horses, mules, supplies! They say I am rich and that it doesn't matter. But, John, if this keeps on I'll be ruined."

"Law and order will put an end to your troubles," said John. "California will soon become a state and we will have a good, strong government."

"The people are more interested in making money than in good government," replied Sutter. "Until they change we will have plenty of trouble."

"They will change, my friend," said John. "Americans believe in good government. In time, law and order will come to this land of gold."

The Miners' City

JOHN had not been to San Francisco since the gold rush began. He knew, of course, that the forty-niners had taken the town by storm. Many had established themselves in business instead of going on to the gold fields. He expected to see many changes. But he was not prepared to find the town completely different. There were few traces of the sleepy place he remembered. San Francisco, in less than a year, had become a lively, stirring, busy city.

And what a city! A city of noisy, newly-rich miners in from the diggings, a city of newly-arrived gold seekers, a city of tents and shanties and muddy streets, a city of excitement and confusion—it was the miners' city.

"I can hardly believe my own eyes," John said as he and Sutter walked down a crowded street. "All these hotels, houses, stores, and shops, and this wild, unruly mob of thousands of men."

The two friends stopped now and then to look into the stores and shops. The goods were expensive and most of them not well made. But everything the miners needed could be found in the shops along the way. There were many stores where only mining tools were sold. Clerks in other stores were busy selling the familiar red and blue flannel shirts, the sturdy, high boots, broad-brimmed hats, and other articles of rough mining clothes to eager buyers.

At a corner, John and Sutter said good-by to each other, promising to meet later in the day. Sutter went across the street to the office of a business friend.

John stepped aside to let a laughing group of red-shirted miners pass. One of the men turned and looked back. The man was the homesick miner who had worked at Bidwell's Bar. He said something to his companions, and then he walked back to John.

As the miner and John shook hands, John said, "I can see that you have had mail from home."

"Yes, and the letters saved my life," the man grinned. "Another ship has just come in with more mail. We're on our way to the post office."

"But it will be hours before the mail is brought ashore. Why don't you wait?" asked John.

"See that crowd!" the miner pointed down the street. In front of a small frame building hundreds of men were forming into long lines. "They know the mail ship is in, too."

"Do you mean that they are going to wait in line until they get their mail?"

"Sure! We always do."

"Well, let's not stand here talking." John and the miner hurried to the post office. The miner looked about for his companions, but could not find them in the noisy crowd.

"Do you get your mail here, too?" he asked as he and John took their places at the end of a line.

"No, I go down to Sutter's Fort to get mine."

The miner shook his head. "We're so far from home and it takes so long to get our letters. That's the hardest part of this life, isn't it?"

John nodded. "I remember when I first came

out here. It took almost a year to let my parents know where I was. Almost another year passed before I heard from them. I'll never forget how happy I was to get their letters."

While they were talking John watched the crowd. The lines were rapidly growing longer and longer. The men shouted and laughed, and excitement ran high. But with all their loud, good humor the men were restless. Many would get letters from home and many would be disappointed. The uncertainty made the endless hours of waiting a great strain.

John was about to say good-by to his miner friend when he felt someone touch his coat sleeve. He turned quickly and looked down into the upturned face of a boy not more than sixteen years of age.

"Say, Mister, will you sell your place in line to me?" the boy asked. "I'll give you twenty-five dollars' worth of gold, Mister."

John was startled by the pleading look in the boy's eyes. "He's only a youngster," he said to himself. "Poor, homesick kid."

"Please do," the boy begged. He pulled a buckskin bag from his pocket and shoved it into John's hands. "There's fifty dollars' worth of gold in the bag. It's all I have, but you can have it. I just must get in line, Mister. I may get a letter from my mother." He burst into tears.

A silence fell over the noisy crowd. John put his arms around the sobbing boy, and said, "You may have my place."

"Oh, thank you."

"And here's your gold," John added.

"But it's yours," the boy protested.

"I have no business here," John explained. "I was just talking to a friend."

As John stepped out of line the men cheered. He held up a hand for silence. "This boy," he said when the men were quiet, "is expecting a letter from his mother. What do you say that we buy the first place in line for him?"

"Sure!" the men shouted. "Sure!"

"Good! Then let's take up a collection."

Within a few minutes the boy was standing at the head of the line. The miner who had been first in line refused to accept the gold collected by the men.

"Me! Take gold to help a homesick youngster!" he exclaimed. "I should say not! Give the gold to him." And without another word he walked down the long line to take another place.

"Mister, I don't know how to thank you and the other men," the boy said to John.

"We don't want any thanks, son. By the way, my name is John Bidwell."

"John Bidwell! Are you the man who had a gold bar named after him?"

John smiled and nodded.

The boy whistled. "Gee, Mr. Bidwell, I'm glad to meet you."

John patted the youngster's shoulders and left. He laughed softly as he heard the boy say to the men, "That's my new friend, John Bidwell. Why, next to Captain Sutter, I guess he's the most famous man in California."

John strode on, whistling to himself. The rush and bustle of the city thrilled him. What if the buildings were cheap and ugly? What if the streets were mudholes during the rainy season and dusty the rest of the year? What difference did it make?

San Francisco already had something more important. It had the strength, the stubborn strength of the forty-niners. Their spirit of never-say-die would in time bring order, beauty, and charm to the city of the Golden Gate.

John thought of other shanty and tent towns being built by the forty-niners. There was Sacramento, for instance, and Stockton some forty miles south. There was Marysville in the north not far from his bar. The little inland towns were on rivers, and were growing up as supply centers for the diggings.

The forty-niners had accomplished much in a year. They had panned out more than forty million dollars' worth of gold. The gold had been shipped to the markets of the world and the wealth was lost to California.

But the forty-niners were not only miners. They were builders of a country. They were building the future greatness of California. They were sturdy, eager to get ahead, and often reckless. But they always stood on their own feet and solved their own problems. They were men — men of vision—of courage.

As John walked along the crowded streets of San Francisco he was proud of the forty-niners. It was their city.

He stopped to locate the store of his business friends. Quickly he read the signs hanging over the doors of the shops on both sides of the street. One sign carried the word "EXPRESS" in bold, black letters. John's heart leaped as he read it.

Express! The forty-niners had taken over the problem of transportation. The old, slow methods had failed to meet their needs. They demanded speed—speed—and more speed.

Express! Pictures of stagecoaches drawn by foam-covered, galloping horses flashed through John's mind. He saw supply wagons rattling over rough roads leading to the gold fields.

"I knew they would do it," he laughed.

"Knew what?" a passing miner asked.

John pointed to the sign.

"Oh, the Express," said the miner. "There are four other express companies in the city. They are just getting started here. Man alive," he added, as he went on his way, "we need them!"

John hurried to the express office. He introduced himself to the young man who owned the new company. The man had been a stagecoach driver in the East and had come to California to start his own express line.

"Others can pan for gold," the man said. "I'll stick to the job I know and love. But it is going to be harder to establish a line out here than I thought it would be."

"Why do you say that?" John asked.

"You can't drive stagecoaches over oxcart paths and pack-mule trails. If there is a good road anywhere in California, I'd like to know where it is."

"So would I," John laughed.

"Before I landed out here I planned to have a line straight through to the gold fields. I soon changed my mind. The fifty-mile stretch from here to San Jose will be all I can handle."

"That will be a good stretch," said John. "The

flat land along the bay is a natural roadway."

"Yes, but San Jose is too far from the diggings."

"San Jose is becoming an important place," said John. "Already it is a supply base for the diggings. And another thing, San Jose is our capital city. Many men will be going there on official business. They will prefer to travel by stagecoach because it is much faster than by boat."

"Yes," the man agreed, "but just the same I want to get through to the diggings and I want to establish a permanent express line. That's the way it is done in the East, you know."

"The East is a settled country. California is not, and it will not be until the gold rush is over," said John. "The miners are forever rushing about seeking richer diggings. They are—"

"Well," interrupted the man, "no wonder you haven't a good transportation system."

John laughed. "We didn't need one until you forty-niners came out here."

The men talked on, discussing the many problems of transportation. It was a big job, a tough job, to organize an express line.

Capable drivers had to be hired to handle the fast horses and the expensive stagecoaches. Other men had to be employed to work in the stations along the way. At each station the horses would be changed, for speed must be maintained at all costs. Meals had to be prepared for the passengers, and at overnight stops, rooms had to be provided for them.

Express was a big business and a very important one. It was like a mighty chain linking together cities, towns, and scattered mining camps.

"We need a good speedy transportation system," said John. "Newly-arrived gold seekers and supplies of all kinds must be taken to the diggings. The gold must be hauled back. And another thing, the mail from home must be carried to the mining camps."

"I'll haul the passengers and gold," spoke up the man, "but I'll not bother with the mail. There isn't enough money in it."

"You haven't been out here very long, have you?" said John quietly.

"No, only a few weeks. Why?"

"Have you been over to the post office?"

"No, I won't get any mail from home for a few months so I haven't been there."

"Then you haven't seen the men standing in line for hours waiting to get their letters," said John. "Well, I have and I tell you these men need mail from home brought right into their camps just as much as they need supplies. They are lonely men. They will pay almost any price to get mail delivered to them at the diggings. And I tell you, it's up to the Express to get the mail through."

"I suppose it can be done."

"Sure it can," said John. "The Express must not be used only as a faster system of transportation. The Express must also speed communication. The two go hand in hand. Both are important to the progress and to the future greatness of California."

"You certainly are a booster for California."

"California is my home," said John. "I believe in its future."

Law of the Mining Camps

THE WINTER MONTHS passed slowly for the miners. At first they had enjoyed the exciting life in the cities and towns. Within a short time, however, they were anxious to return to the diggings. They were tired of doing nothing, the noisy celebrations, the gray, rainy days.

Then, too, many needed to get back to work. They had spent most of their hard-earned wealth in wild, reckless living. Many had gambled away their gold and others had been cheated and robbed.

The early signs of the coming spring sent the men rushing to the gold fields. Stagecoaches and wagons rattled and bumped along the express lines. Mining camps echoed with the shouts of men, glad to be on the job again. This was the life, they agreed. Why, with a little luck a fellow could strike it rich!

In the north John and the miners who had spent

the winter at his ranch were heading for Bidwell's Bar. They expected to be the first party to reach the bar. They were, therefore, surprised to find fifty miners already at work in the icy waters of the Feather River. Most of the men were panning for gold in the usual manner. A few, however, were using a new machine called a cradle, or rocker.

The machine was a box three to five feet long and about eight inches deep. The pay dirt was shoveled into the box. Then while the water was

poured over the dirt the box was rocked back and forth like a baby's cradle. The gold sank to the bottom and the dirt and gravel were washed away. It took a long time to wash away a bucket of pay dirt, but it was faster than panning for gold.

One group of five men were using another new machine. It was a large wooden box called a long tom. It was like the cradle only much longer and bigger and could hold more pay dirt. The long tom, however, was expensive for it was made of lumber, and lumber was still very scarce.

"The machines certainly are improvements over the slow, tiresome panning method," John said to the new miners at the bar. "Where did you buy them?"

"We bought ours at Marysville," a man replied. "But you can get them at most mining stores now."

"I must get some for my trading post," said John.

"Get a cradle for me," said a man in John's party.

"Get one for me, too," said another.

Three men quickly decided to work together and they wanted a long tom. Four others became partners on the spot and they, too, ordered a long tom.

"I'll get them," John promised.

"Cradles! Long toms!" scoffed a man. "You can have your fancy machines! I'll pan out my gold."

Most of the miners agreed. The pan, pick, and shovel were still their favorite tools.

"Bidwell," said a tall, keen-eyed miner, "we're

having some trouble with a couple of men in camp. We want you to settle the dispute."

"What is the matter?" asked John.

"Well," the miner replied, "when we came up here we decided to adopt the camp laws used in the diggings around Coloma. Now, according to these laws, the gold-bearing ground must be equally shared by the men in camp. In order to do this here each man is entitled to stake out a claim twenty-four feet square. The claim is his as long as he works it."

"What can he do if the claim is not a good one?" questioned John.

"He can stake out another claim whenever he wishes," the miner answered. "But he can work only one claim at a time."

"That is a fair law and should be enforced."

"Yes, but the men causing the trouble have staked out more ground than they are entitled to claim. One of the men jumped my claim. He said it belonged to him last year."

"And you let him keep it?"

"I didn't want any trouble with you, Bidwell.

The man said you were his friend and he—"

"No claim jumper is a friend of mine," interrupted John. "I know from experience that claim jumpers are greedy, lawless men."

"Then you are on our side?"

"I'm for law and order," John replied in a firm voice. "And if you have set up camp laws they must be obeyed by everyone."

"Good!" the miners exclaimed.

"Now, I want to talk to those troublemakers," said John. "Where are they?"

"They are working on their claims," a miner answered. "Shall I tell them you want to see them?"

John nodded.

The miner left the group. In a few minutes he returned, followed by two rough-looking men.

"Hello, Bidwell," the men said with a great show of pretending they were glad to see him.

"Hello," John replied. "I understand," he continued, "that you are causing a little unnecessary trouble here at the bar."

"We can explain everything."

"Stake out your claims according to the law of the mining camps and I'll listen to your story."

"And if we don't?" sneered one of the men.

"Then you'll have exactly one hour to leave the bar," John answered. He pulled his watch from his pocket, glanced at it and slipped it back into his pocket again. "It's four o'clock. You have until five to make up your minds. I'll wait here for your decision."

Muttering to each other the men walked slowly away. They looked back once and then walked on to their claims downstream.

"Let's run them out of camp," spoke up a miner.

"No," said John quickly. "They have an hour to decide what they want to do. You asked me to settle this dispute. Let me handle it my own way. Now, go back to work," he added. He turned to the members of his party. "Stake out your claims, boys."

Although the miners protested, they finally agreed to do as John wished. They remained near by, however, and watched him with anxious eyes.

John waited quietly. Occasionally he looked at

his watch, and once he shook it, thinking it had stopped. Slowly the time dragged by.

A few minutes before five o'clock a miner shouted, "Here they come, Bidwell!"

At once all the miners dropped their tools and rushed to where John was standing. In silence they formed a half circle around him.

When the two men were near, John stepped forward. Intently he studied their bearded faces. They refused to meet his steady gaze.

"You win, Bidwell," the older man said. "We'll stake out our lawful claims in the morning."

"You'll stake them out right now," John replied. "And I'll measure them."

"Well—all right," the men agreed.

That night as the miners cooked their suppers of beans and salt pork, they laughed and talked as though nothing had happened. Later they gathered around a big campfire and sang their favorite songs. All was well at Bidwell's Bar.

In the morning, before sunrise, John was awakened by the angry voices of shouting men. He jumped out of his bunk and hurriedly began to dress. As he was pulling on his high, black boots a knock sounded on the door of his shanty.

"Come in," John called.

The door was thrown open. A wild-eyed, excited miner burst into the room.

"I've been robbed!" he cried. "Robbed of every ounce of gold dust. Two thousand dollars' worth of gold!"

"What!"

"I tell you I've been robbed. They did it. They did it—those sneaking claim jumpers. If I can find them I'll shoot them. I'll kill them."

"Just a minute. Just a minute," said John trying to calm the miner. "What do you mean—if you can find them? Have they left camp?"

"Yes! Yes! They have pulled up stakes, taken their tent, pack animals, and cleared out."

"They can't be far from here. We'll get them and bring them back to camp."

While they were talking other miners crowded into the small room. They were shouting, interrupting one another, trying to tell their stories of the robbery.

"I heard a noise outside my tent about three o'clock this morning," said a miner.

"It was four," spoke up his partner.

"Let's find these scoundrels," shouted another, "and hang them to show other robbers what to expect here at the bar."

"Men! Men!" John held up his right hand for silence. "There must be a better way to solve this problem. Surely the law of the mining camps must provide orderly trials for these men. Remember they are not criminals until they have been proved guilty by law."

He paused and looked from man to man. They remained silent.

"Can't you see that I am right?" John asked. "Can't you see that without justice we have no law—no order?"

"I guess you're right, Bidwell," a miner finally said. "What do you want us to do?"

"I want these men to have a fair trial. If they are innocent, they must be cleared of the charges of robbery. If they are guilty, then they must be punished. That is all I want."

"All right, Bidwell. We'll do as you say."

"You know, boys," a bearded old miner said scratching his head, "we almost let our tempers get the best of us. Thanks, Bidwell, for panning us out of trouble."

"Yes," the others agreed. "Thanks a lot."

John smiled quickly. "I was doing a little panning for myself, too. We are all in this together, so let's keep on the side of law and order."

The miners cheered.

"Now, let's get down to business," said John. "We must find the men and bring them back to camp. More than likely they are heading for Marysville. I know a place or two along the way where they could hide out for a few days." He nodded to three miners. "Come," he added, "let's hit the trail."

John and his companions were soon on their way. They were mounted on mules and rode at a slow, but steady pace. No amount of urging could make the sure-footed, sturdy little animals hurry unless they wanted to, for they were as stubborn as they were reliable.

As John suspected the robbers were found in a hideout off the trail leading to Marysville. The searching party closed in on the men so quietly and swiftly they had no time to put up a fight. They were disarmed at once. Although they loudly protested their innocence the stolen gold was found in their packs.

They were terror-stricken when John told them they were to stand trial for their crimes. They begged and pleaded not to be taken back to camp. They were certain the miners would hang them.

But John was firm. Back to the bar they went. That very night they were put on trial. The mining law was new and it might have many faults. But—delay was never one of them.

Everything had been attended to even before the guilty pair had been found. They were guilty all right, but they would get a fair trial! Twelve miners had been chosen to make up the jury. John was made judge of the newly-formed court.

At first John declined to become judge. He wanted the miners to run the court and enforce their own laws. They explained that since he was

their senator, he had legal experience and they had none. Also they admired and respected him.

John thanked the miners and accepted the highest honor they could give him. Then, without wasting more time, John and the members of the jury took their places by a campfire. The miners gathered around them. The men charged with robbery were brought in and the trial began.

In less than ten minutes the trial was over. The men had been found guilty by law. The stolen gold was given back to the rightful owner. The men were sentenced to leave the bar and never to return, if they wished to save their worthless necks. If they did return, they would be hanged from the first tree in sight.

That was the law of the mining camps—swift and perhaps harsh, but to the point. There was no need for fancy legal forms. It was merely a question of right or wrong, guilty or innocent. It was the law of strong men determined to live decently.

Silently the miners watched the two robbers leave camp. When they were lost in the darkness of the night the miners turned again to John.

"By jingo," spoke up the miner who had recovered his gold, "I can't help but feel sorry for those two scoundrels."

"Well, I'm not," said another.

"I'm sorry for them and sorry for us, too," said John. "You see, in the past, we men lived together and trusted one another. Now, greedy, lawless men have come to the gold fields. From now on, there will be plenty of trouble in the diggings."

The Thirty-first Star

LIFE at the bar went on much as usual. Day after day more men arrived. They staked out their claims and went to work.

Little was said about the recent trial and punishment of the robbers. But their crime had left its mark. The miners no longer trusted one another as they had in the past.

New arrivals were looked upon with suspicion until they proved to be honest and hard-working men. They were questioned about the rules used in other camps. Most of the laws were quickly adopted, and in this way the law of the mining camps spread throughout the diggings.

John was pleased with the miners at the bar. They were good customers at his trading post and good friends in camp.

One night after John closed his store, he joined the men singing around a big campfire. He sang with them awhile and then told them that he was leaving the bar for several months.

"I'm going to Washington, D. C.," he said.

"How will we get our supplies?" asked a miner.

"One of my clerks will be in charge of the store," John replied. "And in a few weeks a merchant from Marysville is opening a trading post."

"But he doesn't know us," another man said. "What will we do, if we get strapped?"

"Haven't I always grubstaked you when you needed help?" asked John.

"Sure!" the shout went up around the campfire. "But we can't depend upon the new trader to help us."

"No, but I have left orders that whenever you run out of luck you are to be grubstaked."

"Thanks, Bidwell. Thanks."

"Why are you going to Washington?" a miner asked.

"I am going with another man on official business," John answered. "We were chosen to take a block of gold quartz to the capital city. A great and beautiful monument is being built there in honor of George Washington. The golden block is California's gift to his memory. Many countries are sending historic stones and markers to be fitted into the monument. Many states in the Union are also sending—"

"Well," interrupted a man. "I wouldn't give them the gold until they admit us to the Union."

John and the miners laughed.

"Well, I wouldn't," the man insisted. "No, sir! It's not fair to keep us out of the Union. California has every right to become a state."

"I shall do everything I can to help our cause. The Congress of the United States is considering our request and I think we will be admitted. President Taylor favors our cause."

"Old Rough and Ready!" said a miner. "I fought with him in the Mexican War. You can count on him."

In July, some weeks later, John and his companion arrived in Washington. They were saddened to learn of the sudden death of President Taylor. How would the death of the soldier-president affect California? Would the new president, Millard Fillmore, be for or against California's admission to the Union?

John and his friends delivered the golden block to the mayor of Washington. He accepted the gift, and today it can be seen in the Washington Monument along with other gifts honoring the memory of the Father of Our Country.

All summer, in spite of the heat, John remained in the capital city. All summer he loyally worked for the cause dear to his heart.

Then at last, on September 9, 1850, California was admitted to the Union. The papers were signed by President Filmore and given to John. He was given the official papers to take back to California.

Without delay John made ready for the homeward trip. Since he had come East by the Panama route he had planned to return by way of the Horn. The Panama route was much shorter, however, and he decided to make the same trip again. The glad news he was carrying made him eager to arrive home as quickly as possible.

John sailed from New York City on the first

boat leaving for Panama. Five weeks later, on board another boat, he sailed into the Golden Gate.

San Francisco went wild when the news was told that California had become a state. All business stopped while the people celebrated. Bells rang, cannon boomed, bands played, bonfires blazed.

When John gave the official papers to the governor he said, "It is a great honor to deliver these papers to you."

"No man deserves the honor more than you, Bidwell," the governor replied. "Nine years ago you brought the first overland party of settlers into this golden, sunny land. It is right and proper that you should bring this glorious message."

As the news spread over the state, celebrations were held in cities, towns, and mining camps. At last the thirty-first star had been added to the Stars and Stripes. Proudly California took its place in the United States of America.

At Bidwell's Bar the miners celebrated for days. Then just as they started to work again John arrived. The men gave him a noisy welcome. They held a special celebration in his honor.

John was amazed at the growth of the bar. The mining camp had taken on the airs of a little town. Streets had been laid out, several trading posts and a small hotel had been built. There were even a few frame houses.

"And that's not all," said a miner. "We have an express office, too. Shortly after you left, Bidwell, a young man started an express line from here to Marysville."

"He's a go-getter," said another. "He will haul anything—gold, passengers, mail, supplies. We're all for him here at the bar."

"You know," spoke up a miner, "I worry about the kid whenever he hauls gold to Marysville. He is leaving tomorrow with twenty thousand dollars' worth of gold." The miner shook his head.

"Have you had any trouble at the bar recently?" asked John.

"We haven't had any trouble," the miner answered. "But in the camps around Coloma scarcely a day passes without a robbery or a murder."

While John and the miners were talking they

were joined by the expressman. John liked the young man at once, and understood why he was popular at the bar. He had the firm handclasp, and steady, direct gaze of a man who could make his own way anywhere.

"I'm glad to meet you," said John. "We certainly needed an express line up here. And according to the miners, you're doing a good job."

"Well, I'm busy," the young man replied. "You see, I do all the work myself because I have only one wagon and four mules. But I've made some money now, and in the spring I plan to extend my line. I'm going to buy two stagecoaches, some fast horses, and hire a few men to work for me." He smiled quickly. "Oh, I've made a lot of plans for next year."

"One of your plans had better be to hire guards to ride with you when you carry gold," said a miner. "I tell you, kid, you're headed for trouble."

"Tomorrow is the last time I'll carry gold alone," the expressman said. He added with a little laugh, "I'll be glad when the trip is over."

"I'll make the trip with you," said John.

"No, thanks, Bidwell, I'll make it alone."

In the morning, shortly after breakfast, the expressman was on his way. Just before his wagon disappeared around a turn in the trail he looked back and waved his hat to the watching men. They waved their dust-covered hats in answer.

Then laughing and talking the men made ready for the day's work. The miners gathered up their tools and hurried to their claims. John and the owners of the little stores and hotel talked a while longer and then they also went to work.

Early in the afternoon John decided to walk down to the river. He left the trading post and strode along whistling to himself. The bar was quiet except for the familiar harsh, grating sounds made by the picks and shovels of busy miners.

Suddenly he stopped. His keen ears had caught another sound—a sound on the trail. He listened intently. The sound came nearer and nearer.

Then in a flash he realized that it was a wagon being drawn over the rough, mountain trail by runaway horses or mules. A second later, around the bend in the trail, raced four mules dragging

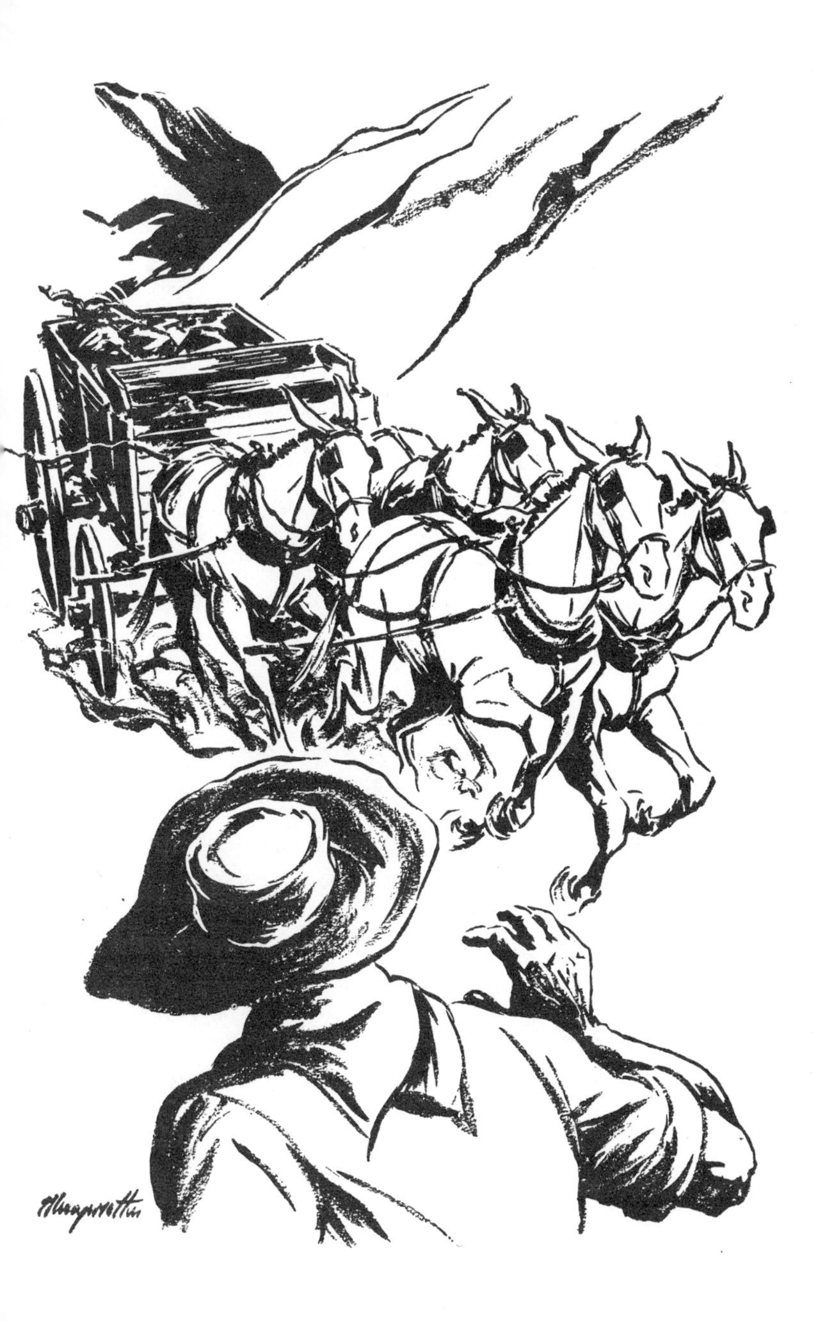

a rattling express wagon — and no driver.

"Men!" shouted John to the miners. "Come!" He ran back down the street.

The mules came to a quick stop in front of the little express office. They stood waiting for their master to unhitch them. But he was lying on the floor of the wagon in a pool of blood.

With one leap John was in the wagon and kneeling beside the young expressman. The man was alive, but he was unconscious. His right arm was wrapped in a blood-soaked bandage. Strips of cloth had been torn from his shirt and tied around the arm. They told of the desperate attempts he had made to stop the flow of blood.

By now the miners had surrounded the wagon.

"He is still alive," John said. "Here, help me," he added. "Let's carry him into the office."

An hour later the young man stirred and slowly opened his eyes.

"You'll be all right now," John said leaning over him. "Fight and you'll make it."

"The gold is safe," the man whispered.

"Forget the gold."

"No," the man shook his head. "They got me on my last trip. But they didn't get the gold. Tell the boys it's safe in the wagon."

"I'll tell them. Don't talk now."

"Let me talk. I know I can't make it."

Quietly the young expressman told of his last trip. He had been stopped by two masked men, but he had fought his way out of the holdup. After the bandits fled he somehow managed to turn his mules around on the trail and headed them back to the bar. On the way he had fallen unconscious from the driver's seat.

"I wounded both robbers," he said. "They must be on the trail somewhere."

"If they are, we'll find them," John promised.

"Tell the boys—"

The sentence was never finished.

John bowed his head. He stood for a minute beside the still figure of the young man who had given his life to protect the gold he carried. Then slowly John walked to the door. He opened it and stepped outside where the anxious miners were waiting.

"He didn't make it, boys," said John in a low voice.

"Did he say anything?" they asked.

"Yes," John answered. "He said that he wounded the bandits. They must be on the trail somewhere."

"We'll get them!" the miners shouted. "They'll hang for this."

John held up his hand. "Your gold is safe. It's in the wagon."

A silence fell over the group. Somehow the gold was not important now. A man had died, a man who had been their friend.

The miners looked at one another. At last a man stepped forward.

"Bidwell," he said, "I suppose you're going to tell us that the law of the mining camp will now take over. But we have already decided that we are going to handle this one ourselves."

"I'm with you," John replied quickly. "The law of the mining camps has taken over the law of the trail. Come on, men!" he ordered, "let's ride!"

Gold and the Lives of Men

JOHN and the men followed the trail to Marysville. Miles from the bar they came to the place of the holdup. Signs of the struggle made the place easy to spot. The wheel marks of the express wagon and the hoofprints of the mules showed clearly where the expressman had turned his team around on the trail.

Tight-lipped and grim, the men rode on. A short distance beyond they found the bodies of the dead robbers. Without a word the men buried the bandits and then headed back to the bar.

Within a few weeks the cold fall rains ended the year's work in the diggings. As before, most of the miners rushed to San Francisco or to other lively cities. A few bought enough supplies to last all winter and remained at the bar. Others rode with John to his ranch at Chico Creek.

In February John bought the remaining half

of the ranch. At last Rancho Chico was his—all of it—more than twenty-two thousand acres.

John gave up his mining interests in order to give all his time to improving his land. In the spring, however, it was with a touch of regret that he said good-by to the miners when they returned to the bar.

"I shall miss you," he said. "Good luck to you."

"You'll be back," said a miner. "The gold fever won't let you settle down in one place very long."

John looked out across the valley. Fifteen miles to the east rose the blue foothills of the Sierra Nevada Mountains.

Once that mighty range had blocked his way into California. Once its snow-capped peaks had stood between him and his dream. But his dream had finally come true. He had worked for and earned the land he loved. And now the Sierra Nevada Mountains marked the eastern boundary of his ranch.

"You are wrong," John replied. "This is where I'll spend the rest of my life."

"I couldn't settle down as long as there is any

excitement in the gold fields," said a man.

John smiled. "Maybe if I had come out here during the gold rush, I, too, would want only excitement. But I came out here in '41 for just one reason. I wanted land. For ten long years I had to work and plan and save my money to buy the land I wanted. Now I have it. Rancho Chico is mine!"

"Well, boys, I guess we lose," said a miner. "Let's get started." He held out his hand to John. "The bar won't be the same without you, Bidwell."

"Indeed, it won't!" the others exclaimed.

"Thanks, men. Thanks a lot."

John watched the men ride away. He wondered what adventures they would share. Would they strike it rich, or would they roam from camp to camp in their restless search for excitement and gold?

He was a little sorry for them because he felt they were not building for the future. Then he threw back his head and laughed. "And they are sorry for me, too. I can just hear them saying, 'Poor Bidwell! How can he settle down during these exciting times?' " He laughed softly. "They don't know the real adventure of owning land is to develop it. I'm going to meet that challenge. Rancho Chico shall be the finest ranch in the state of California."

Carefully John made his plans. It would take many years to do all he wanted to do. Each year he would make new improvements and increase the size of his fields and herds of cattle. In time his ranch would be the finest, the most productive ranch in California.

John hired the Indians living on his land to work for him. He paid them good wages and treated them fairly. He hired dependable white men as foremen. They were to supervise the many jobs on the ranch.

John's kindness won the friendship of all the Indians. To show their gratitude they worked harder than ever. When John rode to their village, old and young welcomed him with cheers and shouts. And always there was a wild scramble as the boys fought for the honor of holding his prancing horse.

In the busy weeks new fields were plowed and planted to wheat. Already John had decided that wheat was to be his main crop. More herds of cattle were purchased and turned out to grow sleek and fat in the green pastures. Acres of land were prepared for vegetable gardens and orchards.

Late in the summer John bought a large herd of cattle from a man living on a ranch near Sacramento. While a party of his Indians drove the herd back to Rancho Chico, John went on to the city of Sacramento.

The city had grown a great deal, but he was not surprised. Nothing the forty-niners could do would surprise him anymore. He was used to the rapid changes they made. But he never ceased to marvel at their energy and ability.

A dozen express companies had opened offices in the river city. Each had more business than it could handle. Almost any hour of the day or night stagecoaches and supply wagons could be seen leaving for the gold fields. Great clouds of dust were kicked up by the horse and mule teams.

The dust had scarcely settled when other stage-coaches and express wagons rolled in from the diggings. They were loaded with passengers and gold.

All too often a returning expressman was held up by highway bandits. Sometimes the driver was able to shoot his way out of trouble. But more often he was forced to turn the gold over to the bandits.

Hoping to stop these crimes the companies hired armed guards to ride with the drivers. In spite of all the safety measures the robberies steadily increased.

The day after John's arrival in Sacramento another stagecoach robbery took place. This time both the driver and guard were killed. One of the ten passengers, a red-shirted miner, brought the stagecoach in to its home station.

The news of the holdup spread quickly. Angry men gathered at the express office. John pushed his way through the crowd to the miner's side.

"They didn't have a chance," the miner was saying. "We were rattling along at a good pace when suddenly two shots rang out. The guard and driver were dead before they hit the ground. In a minute the bandits had the gold and were gone."

"Surely ten passengers could have saved the gold!" called a man far back in the crowd. "Why didn't you put up a fight?"

"Who said that?" the miner demanded.

"I did." A well-dressed man came forward. He shook his silver-handled cane at the miner.

"Well! Well!" the miner said. Slowly he looked the man over from his brightly polished boots to his white gloves and tall silk hat.

"You know it's a funny thing," the miner continued. "But when you are looking into the barrel of a loaded gun you just aren't thinking about gold. No, sir, brother, you are thinking about saving your skin."

"Maybe you're right," the man replied, "but where I live in the East—"

"This is California," interrupted John.

"Good for you, Bidwell," the crowd shouted.

"Stranger," said the miner, "after you have been

out here awhile you will learn never to say anything against California when John Bidwell is around."

"Well, now, Bidwell," the stranger said, "I think California is a great country. But the newspapers back home are full of the murders and robberies committed out here."

"Do your newspapers print the stories of the cities built by the forty-niners?" John asked. "Do they tell of the transportation systems? Do they tell of the mining camps of homesick, lonely men?"

"Well, yes, a little. But these crimes, Bidwell, they are a disgrace to the state."

"I agree with you, sir. But for every crime committed there are hundreds of proofs of real friendship and honor. For every bandit and lawbreaker there are a thousand honest, sturdy men. They are fighting for law and order. They will win."

"You seem very sure."

"I am sure. I know these men. I know what they can do."

"I hope you are right, Bidwell," the man replied. He glanced at the crowd. Then, swinging his cane, he walked quickly away without another word.

"Well, of all the stuffed shirts!" a miner exclaimed. He imitated the man's haughty manner.

The men howled with laughter. Then for an hour or more they talked soberly with John. They were determined to put an end to the highway robberies. But how to do it was a real problem. Always the holdups occurred at lonely spots along the roads. Always the bandits struck quickly and even more swiftly they escaped to secret mountain hideouts.

"Another advantage they have," said John, "is that the express lines run on schedules. That makes it easy for the bandits to know where the stagecoaches are all the time. They know when a stagecoach leaves a mining camp and the road it will follow."

"All the advantages are on their side," said a miner. "How can we fight them to a finish?"

"It will be a long, tough fight," John admitted. "But we will win."

Most of the men agreed with John. Others were discouraged. But as the crowd broke up, each man promised to carry on the fight for law and order.

John walked on alone. The noises of the city streets made him eager to return to Rancho Chico. He wondered if the Indians had arrived safely with the herd of cattle. He thought of the new fields of wheat tossing in the summer breeze.

His thoughts were interrupted by a man calling to him. At once he recognized the familiar voice of Captain Sutter.

"Why, Captain, I am glad to see you," he said shaking hands with his old friend. "What are you doing in Sacramento?"

"Trouble! Trouble! The same old story," Sutter replied. "Greedy, lawless men. They are trying to take my land from me."

The captain went on to explain how squatters were causing him trouble. A squatter, like a claim jumper, had no respect for another person's property. He simply moved onto the land and claimed it as his own.

"The United States government has not as yet approved the grants given to me by Mexico,"

Sutter continued. "So in all fairness I cannot blame the squatters. Some of them have told me that as soon as the government approves my claims, they will move. Others say they will remain no matter what happens."

"Your land grants will be approved," said John.

"I'm not so sure," said Sutter. "There is a great deal of talk that no man should be allowed to hold as much land as I own. I have given my land grant papers to my lawyer here in Sacramento."

Sutter drew a deep breath. "If anything should happen to those papers I would have nothing to prove my title to the land. But," he added, "let's not talk about my troubles. I was on my way to the fort. Do you want to go with me?"

"Yes. Are you still renting the fort?"

The captain shook his head, but made no other reply.

The two-mile walk to the fort was made in silence. As they neared the fort John's heart sank. The once mighty fortress was falling to ruin. Its heavy wooden gates had been torn down and carried away, leaving wide gaps in the crumbling adobe walls. The once great busy square with its stores and shops was deserted. Only the song of a wild bird broke the deep, deep quiet of the abandoned fort.

For a long time the two men stood in the great square. John was remembering the past glories of the fort, and he knew that Sutter was, too.

Here a wilderness had been conquered and history had been written. Here John and countless new settlers had been welcomed. Here Frémont had outfitted his men. Here the Mexican flag and then later the American flag had flown proudly from the same tall flagpole. Here Jim Marshall had brought the first pieces of shining gold. Here gold seekers by the thousands had rushed. Here was the beginning and the ending of a man's dream.

Pioneer Prince of California

THOUSANDS OF gold seekers continued to arrive in California. Like those who had come earlier, they rushed to the diggings where all were sure they would strike it rich. But as had happened before, most of the gold seekers made little more than enough to pay the sky-high prices for their living expenses.

It was harder to mine for gold because the early miners had panned out the surface pay dirt. Now the gold supply was deeper. To mine it meant new machines and methods.

Thousands left the gold fields to look for jobs in the cities and towns. Many returned to their homes in the East. Others signed up to work for mining companies. Still others clung to their little claims, or roamed from camp to camp—ever seeking richer diggings.

The great boom years of the gold rush were

over. To make matters worse many express companies failed. Banks closed. A panic swept across the land of gold.

Once again men turned to the land, not for gold this time, but to plant and grow crops and harvest them. Thousands of ex-miners took up claims in the fertile valleys. Hundreds squatted on land already belonging to other men.

Sutter, at Hock Farm, could not keep the squatters off his land. They paid no attention to his pleas and he could not drive them away. He no longer had the papers which gave him a clear title to the land. The papers had been destroyed a few years before when someone had set fire to his lawyer's office.

Doggedly, Sutter fought on to save the land he loved. It was his! As long as he lived he would fight for it. But year after year, he lost more and more of his once great empire.

Up at Rancho Chico the passing years had brought success to John Bidwell. His vast ranch was the finest in all California.

Beautiful fields of wheat stretched like golden

banners across the valley. Herds of cattle grazed in the green pastures. Acres of fruit trees were laden with ripening fruit.

The many duties on the ranch kept him very busy. But he found time to plan the little town of Chico growing up on his land. He gave free lots to all who wished to live in the town. He gave land to be used for the sites of churches and other buildings.

Today, Bidwell's Chico is a city of almost ten thousand inhabitants. It is a city of lovely homes, beautiful parks, and tree-lined streets. Chico has not forgotten its generous founder. The city seal bears the picture of John Bidwell, the Pioneer Prince of California.

John Bidwell earned the proud title of Pioneer Prince because he was deeply interested in everything that meant growth for California. He did not seek public office to gain personal glory or power. Only the future—the great future of California was important to him.

In 1864, Bidwell was elected to the Congress of the United States. His understanding of state and national affairs made him a good congressman. His knowledge of agriculture won for him the important post as chairman of the House Committee on Agriculture.

The Department of Agriculture had been established in 1862. Many thought that the department was not needed. They were trying to do away with it. Others felt that the department was very necessary for it would aid the farmers of the nation.

John was fighting to keep the department. His determined, fearless manner won new friends for him, and also some enemies. One day the men who opposed him warned him to stop fighting. He refused.

"Think of your political future," they said.

"My political future is my own concern—not yours," John replied. "I will never place it above my duty to my country. Good day, gentlemen."

John fought on to save the department. Among the men who agreed with him was Joseph Kennedy. He was an important and wealthy man in Washington.

One December Sunday, as usual, John went to church. After the service, he talked to Mr. Kennedy and met his charming wife and two daughters. John decided that Annie, the younger daughter, was the most beautiful girl he had ever seen.

"Mr. Bidwell," said Mrs. Kennedy, "we would be very happy to have you come to our home for Sunday dinner. Will you be our guest?"

"Yes, thank you." John answered so quickly that they all laughed.

"We shall expect you at one o'clock, Mr. Bidwell," smiled Mrs. Kennedy. "Come, Annie," she added, "our carriage is waiting."

John, hat in hand, stood still while the carriage, drawn by two spirited horses, rolled down the street. Then as it disappeared around a corner he pulled his big, gold watch from his vest pocket.

"Twelve o'clock," he said to himself. "A whole hour to wait. A whole hour!"

Somehow the hour passed and promptly at one o'clock, John entered the stately home of the Kennedys. From that time on he was a frequent and a welcome guest.

All during the winter months John was busy. The fight over the Department of Agriculture had become a bitter one. Neither side was willing to accept defeat. But at last the showdown came.

"The Department of Agriculture is a waste of time and money," a congressman said to the members of the House. "We should not spend one cent to keep it. We must do away with it."

The man talked on and on. Finally it was John's turn. He rose slowly from his chair and faced his audience.

"Gentlemen," he began, "the very foundation of our country is based on agriculture. If you wish to promote the welfare of our country then you must advance the cause of agriculture.

"Our farm land is our greatest source of wealth. The riches we can harvest from the soil will far exceed the wealth of the gold fields."

At the mention of the gold fields every man leaned forward in his chair. A murmur of excitement ran through the House.

"I repeat," John continued, "our farm land, not the gold fields, is our greatest source of wealth.

Gold is mined and then it is gone. But year after year—year after year, the fertile soil will give back to us untold riches.

"Do not do away with the Department of Agriculture. Give it your loyal support. Protect the future of this nation. Let everything else be forgotten. Remember only this, your country's future is in your hands. Gentlemen, I charge you, guard it well!"

John sat down and for a minute the House was very quiet. Then a cheer rang out. Friends, and even some of the men who had opposed John, crowded around him. All praised his brave fight.

But it was the praise of a shy young girl which pleased John most of all. She had won his heart as completely as he had won his fight in Congress. And before his term was over, beautiful Annie Kennedy promised to become his bride.

A year later, April 16, 1868, they were married. Among the guests at the brilliant ceremony were the President of the United States, important members of Congress, and John's best friend, Captain Sutter.

In spite of his own great happiness John was sad when he parted with Sutter. Would they ever meet again? The captain had lost all his land and had left California. He was now living in a little Swiss village in Pennsylvania.

"I'll return someday," Sutter said. "In the meantime I'll stay in the East and fight on."

"I wish you would let me help you, Captain."

"No, John," replied Sutter. "I'll win or lose this fight alone. We have been good friends. And to you and your lovely bride I wish all the happiness in the world. She will grace the mansion you have built for her. Her charm and beauty will attract everyone to her. Your Indians will love her. I hope she will love California as much as we do."

"She will, Captain. I know she will."

"Now I must leave." Sutter held out his hand.

Their handclasp was warm and firm. They did not say good-by to each other. But when they parted there were tears in their eyes.

It was the end of May when John and Annie arrived at Chico. At once Annie fell in love with the Wilderness as she named the mansion.

"Where are your Indians?" she asked.

"Do you want to see them?"

"Oh, yes! And, I hope they like me, too."

Together, hand in hand, they walked to the village. Shyly the Indians came forward. One old squaw said something to Annie and tried to touch her dress. Neither John nor Annie understood what the woman said for she had spoken in a low voice. Later an Indian told them what the woman had said.

"She thought you were an angel," the Indian explained. "Now we call you our Little White Mother."

John looked down into the upturned face of his bride. "Will you be happy here at Rancho Chico?" he asked.

A smile lighted the face of Annie Bidwell. "I'll be happy here," she answered. "This is our home."

Rancho Chico

ONE NIGHT, a few weeks later, Annie and John were sitting in the large, beautiful living room of the mansion.

"But, John, I do want to see the place where you discovered gold," Annie was saying. "Why can't we go to the bar?"

"There isn't anything to see there now," John replied. "The town is deserted. The trip would be too difficult for you. We would have to ride mules and camp out and—"

"I would love it," broke in Annie. She threw back her head and laughed. "Think of sleeping outdoors under the stars. Why, I have never done anything like that in all my life!"

They were interrupted by the excited whisperings of several Indians in the hall. "What is it, John?" Annie asked. Her eyes were wide with terror. "Are they—are they on the warpath?"

"No, no," John laughed. "It is nothing." But he was puzzled, for the Indians never came to the mansion late at night.

Before he could reach the door an Indian entered the room. The Indian glanced at John and hurried to Annie. He dropped to his knees in front of her.

"Little White Mother," his voice was pleading. "My baby sick. You make baby well. You angel."

John saw the swift look of pity replace the fear in Annie's eyes. He heard her say in a low voice, "I will try to make your baby well."

"I'll go with you," spoke up John quickly.

"This is the first time the Indians have come to me for help. Let me go alone, John."

Annie and the Indian were soon on their way to the village. John, standing on the wide porch of the mansion, watched them disappear into the blackness of the night.

"I am going to the village," John said to the Indian servants in the hall.

John hurried down the familiar path. The village was in darkness except for the light of a torch in one straw-covered hut. Near the hut John sat down on the ground.

Now and then the stillness was broken by the cry of the sick baby. Each time Annie's gentle voice was heard as she comforted the infant.

Slowly the hours dragged on. John thought that the night would never end. But at last the rosy colors of the rising sun flooded the eastern sky. The torch in the Indian hut was blown out. In a few minutes Annie was beside John. The smile on her tired face told him that the baby was better.

"Are you all right?" John asked as they walked back to the mansion.

"Yes," Annie replied. "Now, I feel that I truly belong to the West. I have passed my first test."

During the next few days Annie spent many long hours taking care of the baby. Her helpfulness, her quiet charm won the love of all the Indians. When the baby was well again Annie and John left on a trip to the bar.

John marveled at how easily Annie became used to outdoor life. It was hard for him to believe that she was the same girl with whom he had fallen in love. Her wealthy parents had reared her in luxury. Yet here she was learning to make a campfire, riding a mule, sleeping on the ground, and laughing at the dust of the trail. Sturdy, little boots instead of dancing slippers were on her feet. She wore a long, plain dress instead of a silk or satin one from an expensive New York shop.

The bar and the other deserted mining camps near by were disappointments to Annie. It was sad to know that once the camps had been lively, important centers. Men, filled with hopes and dreams, had built them. What had happened to these men, their hopes, and dreams? What had happened to Jim Marshall, the man whose discovery had started the whole mad rush for gold?

"Did James Marshall become a wealthy man?" asked Annie.

"No," John answered. "He is living in poverty in a little mining camp near Coloma."

"How sad."

"Yes, poor Jim. His discovery of gold brought only hard luck to him, and ruin to Captain Sutter."

"Maybe that is the way it had to be."

"Maybe." John drew a deep breath. "And maybe the price is not too great when we remember that gold made California. In 1848, the world knew very little about California. There were only a few thousand people living here and now there are more than half a million. And every year more people are coming out here to live.

"Think what the gold rush did for California. No country in the world was ever settled so quickly. It took the Puritans more than a hundred years to settle New England."

"Yes, but John," said Annie, "they were not gold seekers. They were builders of homes and the founders of our nation."

"I know, Annie. But most of the forty-niners did a pretty good job, too. When the rush for gold was over they didn't quit. They turned to other tasks. Now they are home builders and they are planning ahead for the future."

"And what about you, John? What are your plans?"

"Well, I shall continue to be interested in all national and state affairs," John answered. "Then, of course, I want to keep on developing Rancho Chico. I want to try out new machines and use new methods so I can help other farmers. I want to experiment with wheat and other grains so I can learn to grow better crops. I want to raise better cattle."

"Oh, so many, many plans," laughed Annie. "I can see that you are going to be very busy. Well, I shall be busy, too."

"What are you planning to do?"

"I want to help our Indians. I want to build a church and a school for them. I want them to become Christians. I want them to learn useful occupations and to read and write. I want to hire a doctor to take care of them."

"I shall help you."

"I need your help," said Annie. "I couldn't do it alone." She was silent for a while. Suddenly she said, "Oh, there is much to do. Let's go home and go to work. Let's go home to Rancho Chico."

In the busy years that followed Annie and John found happiness. They helped each other carry out their plans.

John was a welcome visitor to the little school where Annie was teaching the Indians. Often on Sundays they both attended the Indian church instead of going to their church in Chico.

When Annie was made the pastor of their church, the Indians were filled with joy. Now she truly was their Little White Mother. Young men and women came to her to be married. Babies were brought to her to be baptized. She buried their loved ones. Their joys and sorrows were hers.

While Annie was busy with her Indians, John was hard at work, too. Under his direction, Rancho Chico became a great farm where new methods and new machines were tried. Careful records were kept on all the experiments.

One great wheat field of more than a thousand acres was John's special pride. Annie often rode with him to the field and over other parts of the ranch. When, at the Paris Exposition, he won the gold medal for the finest wheat in the world, they were very happy and very proud.

In 1880, the sad news of the death of Captain

John Sutter reached Rancho Chico. The famous old captain had died in Washington. He died still fighting to get back his land.

"I think we both knew when we parted in Washington that we would never meet again," John said. "No pioneer ever did as much for California. He was a great man." His voice broke. "He was my good, good friend."

Five years later, Jim Marshall died. He died in a lonely cabin a few miles from the old mill at Coloma. He had been forgotten by the world. In death he was remembered—for it was his discovery that started the rush for gold.

Captain John A. Sutter, the Swiss, and James Marshall, the jack-of-all-trades, died defeated and discouraged. But the history of California cannot be written without telling the story of their hopes and dreams. They played their parts and won everlasting fame.

History is also written by men who struggle on and win their hopes and dreams. Among these men, the name of John Bidwell stands high.

Rancho Chico was ever dear to his heart and

always he continued to improve it. The estate was more like a great community than one large ranch. Some twenty industries had been developed and each was a ranch in itself.

There were orchards with more than a hundred thousand trees. Millions of pounds of fruit, such as peaches, prunes, oranges, apples, pears, and cherries were gathered each year. There were acres of vegetables and flower gardens and a deer park.

There was a cannery, a packing house, a meat market, and a dairy ranch. There were stock ranches and hay and pasture lands. There were grain ranches and mills to grind the wheat, oats, barley, and other grains.

All this and more John Bidwell had planned and accomplished. This had been the dream of a young boy who had left home with seventy-five dollars in his pocket.

John Bidwell's love for land was deep and real. Mountains had blocked his way and he had crossed them. A gold rush had not stopped him. Business panics had not discouraged him. Nothing had turned him from his course. He fought on and he had won.

* * * *

John Bidwell lived through four great periods of California life before his death April 4, 1900. He knew and loved California while it was still Mexican territory. He knew the marching years of American conquest, the gold-rush years, and the early years of statehood.

He saw Indian trails and oxcart paths become roads for covered wagons and stagecoaches. He lived to see many railroads span the continent.

In the days when laws were not enforced he stood and fought with other men until law and order were firmly established. Always he placed his duty to his country and state above personal gain.

Many men have won fame, but not always have they won the respect of their fellowmen. John Bidwell, the Prince of Pioneers, won both. He was a good American.

Word List

adobe—ə'dōbē

ague—'ā(,)gyü

Bartleson—'bärtᵊl,sən

Californios—kalə'fȯrn(,)yōz

Cheyenne—'shī¦an

Chico—'chē(,)kō

Coloma—kə'lōmə

corral—kə'ral

De Smet—də'smət

Ezekiel Merritt—ə'zēkiᵊl 'merət

Frémont—'frē,mänt

grubstake —'grəb,stāk

Isthmus—'isməs

Juan Alvarado—
(h)wän ¦alvə¦radō

league—'lēg

Mariano Vallejo—
¦märēə¦nō və¦yāhō

mirage—mə'rä|zh

missionaries—'mishə,nerēz

nugget—'nəgət

Polk—'pōk

presidios—prə'sidē,ōz

rancho—'ran(,)chō

Robidoux—'rōbədü

Sacramento—¦sakrə¦ment(,)ō

San Diego—¦san dē'āgō

San Francisco—¦san frən'si(,)skō

San Jose—¦san(h)ō¦zā

Santa Fe—¦santə ¦fā

Sierra Nevada—sē'erə ¦nə'vadə

Sonoma—Sə'nōmə

squatters—'skwä|də(r)s

unconscious—¦ən'känchəs

vaqueros—vä'ke(,)rōs

whoop—h|üp

The system of indicating pronunciation is used by permission of the publishers of *Webster's Third New International Dictionary*, copyright 1961 by G. & C. Merriam Co., Publishers of the Merriam-Webster Dictionaries.